ACE Spelling Activities

Photocopy Masters for use with the ACE Spelling Dictionary

by
David Moseley and Gwyn Singleton

ACE Spelling Activities
MT00380
ISBN-13: 978 1 85503 166 1 1

© David Moseley and Gwyn Singleton
All rights reserved
Design: Tetragon Grafix
Typesetting: Textype Typsesetters
Illustrations: Textype Typsesetters

Printed in the UK for LDA
Abbeygate House, East Road, Cambridge, CB1 1DB, UK

CONTENTS

The answers for all the activity sheets, can be found on pages 113–131.

* If these activities are to be done on a class basis, each person will need a copy of the ACE Spelling Dictionary.

COUNTING SYLLABLES

Aim: the student should be able to say how many syllables there are in any spoken word (up to 4 syllables).

The teacher can work with a group or whole class, asking for individual or group responses. In one-to-one work a partner or older person can read out the words and say whether the responses are correct. The following three stages should be followed.

1 The teacher or tutor (**T**) says a word slowly and taps out the syllables at the same time. The student repeats the word and taps out the syllables. **T** asks, 'How many taps?' This should be done with the following words.

play-ground	win-dow	ba-na-na	mud	un-for-tu-nate
TAP-TAP	TAP-TAP	TAP-TAP-TAP	TAP	TAP-TAP-TAP-TAP

Repeat more slowly if necessary, with the words in a different order.

2 **T** says a word without tapping and asks the student to repeat the word and tap it out. Each time **T** asks, 'How many taps?' This is done with words from the following list until ten words are tapped out correctly.

***	newspaper	**	picture	*	paint	****	television
**	spider	*	mice	**	monster	***	dinosaur
**	postman	**	burglar	***	acrobat	****	politician
**	pancake	***	margarine	****	supermarket	**	kitchen
*	crash	****	helicopter	**	rocket	***	motorbike

3 **T** says a word and simply asks, 'How many syllables?' This is done, taking words at random from the list below, until a success rate of 19/20 is obtained.

**	money	*	shop	**	birthday	**	present
**	bedroom	*	door	***	wallpaper	*	stairs
***	holidays	*	weeks	***	underground	****	underwater
***	crocodile	****	alligator	*	shark	**	danger
****	caterpillar	*	moth	***	butterfly	*	eggs
**	rabbit	****	invisible	*	hat	**	magic
*	win	***	manager	**	football	****	competition
****	everybody	**	children	**	mother	***	grandfather
*	clock	**	morning	***	afternoon	***	yesterday
****	mysterious	***	horrible	***	beautiful	***	exciting

LEARNING HOW TO USE THE ACE DICTIONARY IN 3 EASY LESSONS

The ACE Spelling Dictionary improves spelling and enhances linguistic awareness at all levels of the National Curriculum.

Teachers who adopt the ACE Spelling Dictionary for class use are often surprised that their students find it so easy. As soon as students succeed in finding words, the advantages of the Dictionary become self-evident.

The 60 Second Guide, 'How to Use the ACE Spelling Dictionary', is an excellent introduction, especially when each student has a copy of the Dictionary. However, this initial demonstration does need to be followed up by practice with the Index page, covering the sounds in each section, and looking up words in the Dictionary itself.

The following three lessons provide the practice necessary, and they are suitable for both small groups and whole classes. After following three lessons of direct instruction and practice, students should be able to find any 10 words in under 5 minutes and should then progress to an average speed of 20 seconds per word.

When introducing the Dictionary on a class basis, at least one copy per table is needed. Each of the lessons covers sounds from different sections of the Index – photocopy masters of these sections are provided so that each student can have his/her own copy to work with. Teachers may like to make OHPs of these to use in whole class tuition.

Aims: the student should be able to

a) identify long vowel sounds in a selection of words
b) use the long vowel sounds part of the Index to find the page numbers for a selection of words
c) look up words in the blue part of the Dictionary.

1 Begin with listening and speaking activities, starting with the long vowel animal names: **snail**, **eagle**, **lion**, **goat**, and **newt**.

Ask the students if they can hear certain vowel sounds in each of these animal names. Use correct and incorrect vowel sounds, for example, 'Can you hear (**ae**) in **snail**?' 'Can you hear (**ee**) in **snail**?'

Make the vowel sounds longer and louder if you need to. Continue until responses are confident and correct and then move on to identifying long vowel sounds in other words. For example, 'Can you hear (**ee**) in **fine**?' 'Can you hear (**ae**) in **baby**?'

Again continue until responses are confident and correct.

Selecting a long vowel sound, ask students if they can hear the sound in a variety of words. For example, 'Can you hear (**ae**) in **pail**, **sail**, **tail**, **tile**?' etc.

Finally ask students to give you the vowel sound they can hear in the long vowel animal names, giving a choice of three. For example, 'What is the vowel sound in snail: (**ae**) (**ee**) or (**ie**)?' Continue with different animals and three choices until the sounds in all the long vowel animal names are correctly identified.

2 Practise using the Index to find page numbers. Each student should have a copy of the long vowel part in the middle of the Index (see page 5). Teachers may also like to make an OHP for class tuition.

Beginning with the animal picture words, ask students first to point to the snail picture next to the letters 'ae' which stand for the sound (**ae**). Ask which letter **snail** begins with and have them find the letter, in the alphabet across the top of the page. Then, show them how to move one finger along the line of page numbers and the other finger down, until they meet at a page number. **Snail** is on page 149!

Repeat this exercise with **eagle**, **lion**, **goat** and **newt**. You may need to prompt students with the vowel sound initially, but continue the exercise until the page numbers can be found by the students themselves.

Once students can readily achieve this, asked them to find the page numbers for the following animal words: **ape**, **beaver**, **bison**, **mule**, **poodle**, **reindeer**, **sheep**, **snake**, **tiger**, **whale**.

This time they will need to identify the spelling picture for the vowel sound first. For example, what is the first vowel sound in **tiger**? It is (**ie**), which is the same as in **lion**.

Use these topic lists until students have mastered using the Index to find page numbers.

bacon, cake, cereal, cheese, doughnut, mousse, pie, steak, trifle, tuna

beans, beetroot, coleslaw, cucumber, leeks, maize, peanuts, peas, seaweed, swede

apricot, coconut, dates, grapefruit, lime, peach, pineapple, prunes, raisins, rhubarb

basin, bowl, knife, ladle, microwave, plate, scales, soap, teapot, toast

3 Practise looking up words from one or more of the above lists in the blue part of the Dictionary. After turning to the page, say the word in distinct syllables and have the class say, tap and count the syllables. Make sure they look in the correct column and, if there is a homonym, that they check the meaning. Where the word is not given in plural form (e.g. 'prune'), an 's' should be added. Note that in one case (swede) the target word is in a section which goes on for three pages.

5

Aims: the student should be able to

    a) identify short vowel sounds in a selection of words

    b) use the short vowel sound part of the Index to find the page numbers for a selection of words

    c) look up words in the first two parts of the Dictionary.

1 Begin with listening and speaking activities, starting with the short vowel animal names: **cat**, **elephant**, **pig**, **dog**, **duck**, and **woodpecker.**

Ask the students if they can hear certain vowel sounds in each of these animal names, for example, 'Can you hear (**a**) in **cat**?' 'Can you hear (**e**) in **pig**?'

Make the vowel sounds longer and louder if you need to. Continue until responses are confident and correct and then move on to identifying short vowel sounds in other words. For example, 'Can you hear (**a**) in **active**?' 'Can you hear (**i**) in **big**?'

Again continue until responses are confident and correct.

Selecting a short vowel sound, ask students if they can hear the sound in a variety of words. For example, 'Can you hear (**a**) in **pat**, **fat**, **mat**, **pet**?' etc.

Finally ask students to give you the vowel sound they can hear in the short vowel animal names, giving a choice of three. For example, 'What is the vowel sound in **cat**: (**ae**), (**a**) or (**e**)?' Continue with the different animals and three choices until the sounds in all the short vowel animal names are correctly identified.

2 Practise using the Index to find page numbers first for short and then for both short and long vowel words. Each student should have a copy of the first two parts of the Index (see page 9). Teachers may also like to make an OHP for class tuition. Beginning with the animal picture words, ask students first to point to the cat picture next to the letter 'a', which stands for the sound (**a**). Ask which letter **cat** begins with and have them find the letter, in the alphabet across the top of the page. Then, show them how to move one finger along the line of page numbers and the other finger down, until they meet at a page number. **Cat** is on page 7!

Repeat this exercise with **duck**, **pair**, **watchful** and **woodpecker**.

You may need to prompt students with the vowel sound initially, but continue the exercise until the page numbers can be found by the students themselves.

Once students can readily achieve this, ask them to find the page numbers for the following animal words: **camel**, **donkey**, **frog**, **hedgehog**, **kangaroo**, **leopard**, **monkey**, **pigeon**, **rabbit**, **rook**.

This time they will need to identify the spelling picture for the vowel sound first. For example, what is the first vowel sound in **rabbit**? It is (**a**), which is the same as in **cat**.

Use these topic lists until students have mastered using the short vowel part of the Index.

biscuit, bread, butter, chicken, chocolate, crisps, haddock, jam, popcorn, pudding

broccoli, cabbage, cauliflower, celery, lettuce, mushroom, onion, pepper, pumpkin, spinach

apple, blackberry, cherry, damson, fig, lemon, melon, orange, plum, tangerine

bottle, brush, clock, fridge, matches, mirror, rack, scissors, sieve, whisk

After working with the short vowel part of the Index, ask students to find the page numbers for both short and long vowel words from the following lists. If there is any confusion between short and long vowels, ask for example, 'Is it short (**a**) as in **cat**, or long (**ae**) as in **snail**?' as appropriate.

black, blue, buff, crimson, gold, green, indigo, red, ruby, white

apron, boots, collar, dress, jeans, nightdress, shoes, sweater, tie, vest

bicycle, boat, glider, helicopter, motorcycle, scooter, submarine, train, van, yacht

bus, coach, cycle, ferry, hovercraft, liner, lorry, rocket, tricycle, truck

chewing, cooking, drinking, eating, helping, listening, nodding, sleeping, watching, writing

baker, bricklayer, cook, miner, optician, sailor, scientist, secretary, soldier, teacher

3 Practise looking up words from one or more of the above lists in the Dictionary. After turning to the page, say the word in distinct syllables and have the class say, tap and count the syllables. Make sure they look in the correct column and, if there is a homonym, that they check the meaning. Note that in some cases (apple, biscuit, bus, butter, crimson, drinking, fridge, indigo, matches, optician, orange, spinach, sweater) the target word is in a section which goes on for two or more pages.

Short Vowels

Vowel keys:
- SHORT VOWEL a — ACTIVE CAT
- SHORT VOWEL e — HEALTHY ELEPHANT
- SHORT VOWEL i — BIG PIGLET
- SHORT VOWEL o — WATCHFUL DOG
- SHORT VOWELS u / oo — DUCK AND WOODPECKER

	A	B	C	D	E	F	G	H	I	J	K	L	M	N	O	P	Q	R	S	T	U	V	W	X	Y	Z
a	1	5	7	10	11	12	14	16	17	18	18	19	20	21	22	–	24	24	25	28	–	29	30	30	30	30
e	31	32	33	34	36	39	39	40	41	42	42	43	44	45	45	–	46	47	48	50	52	53	53	54	54	55
i	56	57	59	61	65	68	70	71	72	77	78	79	80	81	81	82	83	84	87	90	91	91	92	–	–	93
o	94	95	96	99	99	100	101	102	102	103	103	104	105	105	106	108	109	110	111	113	113	114	114	115	115	115
u / oo	116	116	118	120	120	121	122	123	124	124	125	126	127	127	128	129	–	130	133	134	136	136	136	–	–	–

Long Vowels

Vowel keys:
- LONG VOWEL a-e — BABY SNAIL
- LONG VOWEL e-e — BREEDING EAGLE
- LONG VOWEL i-e — LIVELY LION
- LONG VOWEL o-e — LONELY GOAT
- LONG VOWELS u-e / oo — SMOOTH NEWT

	A	B	C	D	E	F	G	H	I	J	K	L	M	N	O	P	Q	R	S	T	U	V	W	X	Y	Z
a-e	137	138	139	140	141	142	143	144	144	145	145	146	146	147	147	148	148	149	151	151	152	152	–	–	–	152
e-e	153	154	155	156	157	158	159	160	161	162	163	164	165	165	166	167	167	169	172	173	174	–	–	–	175	175
i-e	176	177	178	178	180	181	182	182	183	184	185	186	187	187	188	189	190	192	193	194	194	–	–	–	–	194
o-e	195	195	196	197	197	198	199	200	200	201	201	202	202	203	204	206	206	207	208	208	209	209	–	–	209	209
u-e / oo	210	211	212	213	214	215	216	216	217	218	218	219	219	220	221	222	223	223	224	224	–	–	–	–	224	224

© LDA ACE Spelling Activities

Aims: the student should be able to

a) identify long vowel sounds, in the third part of the Dictionary, in a selection of words

b) use the Index to find the page numbers for a selection of words

c) look up words in all three parts of the Dictionary.

1 Begin with listening and speaking activities, starting with the animal names from the third part of the Dictionary: **shark**, **bear**, **bird**, **horse**, **oyster** and **owl**.

Ask the students if they can hear certain vowel sounds in each of these animal names, for example, 'Can you hear (**ar**) in **shark**?' 'Can you hear (**or**) in **owl**?'

Make the vowel sounds longer and louder if you need to. Continue until responses are confident and correct and then move on to identifying these long vowel sounds in other words. For example, 'Can you hear (**ar**) in **harmless**?' 'Can you hear (**oi**) in **early**?'

Again continue until the responses are confident and correct.

Selecting one of these long vowel sounds, ask students if they can hear the sound in a variety of words. For example, 'Can you hear (**ar**) in **car**, **fir**, **jar**, **tar**?' etc.

Finally ask students to give you the vowel sound they can hear in the third group of vowel animal names, giving a choice of three. For example, 'What is the vowel sound in **shark**: (**ar**), (**ae**) or (**or**)?'

Continue with the different animals and three choices until the sounds in all the third group of vowel animal names are correctly identified.

2 Practise using the Index to find page numbers for words containing the sounds (**ar**), (**air**), (**er**), (**or**), (**oi**), and (**ou**). Each student should have a copy of the whole Index (see page 13). Teachers may also like to make an OHP for class tuition.

Beginning with the animal picture words, ask students first to point to the shark picture next to the letters 'ar', which stand for the sound (**ar**). Ask which letter **shark** begins with and ask them to point to the letter, in the alphabet across the top of the page.

Then, show them how to move one finger along the line of page numbers and the other finger down, until they meet at a page number. **Shark** is on page 234!

Repeat this exercise with **rare**, **worm**, **warlike**, **oyster** and **sound**.

You may need to prompt students with the vowel sound initially, but continue the exercise until the page numbers can be found by the students themselves.

Once students can readily achieve this, ask them to find the page numbers for the following animal words: **armadillo**, **cow**, **earthworm**, **hound**, **mouse**, **oyster**, **partridge**, **sardine**, **starfish**, **tortoise**.

This time they will need to identify the spelling picture for the vowel sound first. For example, what is the first vowel sound in **partridge**? It is (**ar**), which is the same as in **shark**.

If more practice is needed with the five sounds of the third part of the Index, use the following lists.

burger, cornflakes, flour, lard, marmalade, oil, pork, prawn, sardine, trout

garlic, herbs, parsley, parsnips, pear, soya, sprouts, strawberry, turnip, walnut

boiler, carton, door, fork, jar, larder, margarine, starch, torch, towel

After working with part 3 of the Index, ask students to find the page numbers for words from any of the three parts, using the following lists. If there is any confusion between any pair of patterns, ask for example, 'Is it (**a**) or (**ow**)? Is it (**o**) or (**ar**)?' as appropriate.

aquamarine, brown, cream, ginger, grey, lilac, orange, pink, purple, rose, scarlet, silver, turquoise, violet, yellow

blouse, braces, coat, jacket, jumper, overalls, pullover, sandals, scarf, shorts, skirt, slippers, socks, tights, trousers

brushing, counting, cutting, ironing, learning, marking, painting, reading, serving, sewing, shaving, shopping, sweeping, swimming, working

actress, artist, dentist, doctor, fisherman, hairdresser, joiner, journalist, musician, nurse, plumber, porter, priest, tailor, typist

3 Practise looking up words from one or more of the above lists in the Dictionary. Note that in some cases (aquamarine, cutting, slippers, sweeping, swimming) the target word is in a section which goes on for two or more pages.

Legend of sounds (with mnemonic pictures)

Short vowels:
- SHORT VOWEL a — ACTIVE CAT
- SHORT VOWEL e — HEALTHY ELEPHANT
- SHORT VOWEL i — BIG PIGLET
- SHORT VOWEL o — WATCHFUL DOG
- SHORT VOWELS u / oo — DUCK AND WOODPECKER

Long vowels:
- LONG VOWEL ae — BABY SNAIL
- LONG VOWEL ee — BREEDING EAGLE
- LONG VOWEL ie — LIVELY LION
- LONG VOWEL oe — LONELY GOAT
- LONG VOWELS ue / oo — SMOOTH NEWT
- LONG VOWEL ar — BASKING SHARK
- LONG VOWEL air — RARE BEAR
- LONG VOWEL er — EARLY BIRD WITH WORM
- LONG VOWEL or — WARLIKE HORSE
- LONG VOWEL oi — OYSTER-CATCHER
- LONG VOWEL ou — AN OWL SOUND

Block 1 — Short vowels

Sound	A	B	C	D	E	F	G	H	I	J	K	L	M	N	O	P	Q	R	S	T	U	V	W	X	Y	Z
a (ACTIVE CAT)	1	5	7	10	11	12	14	16	17	18	19	20	21	--	22	24	24	25	28	29	--	30	30	--	30	30
e (HEALTHY ELEPHANT)	31	32	33	34	36	39	39	40	41	42	42	43	44	45	45	46	47	48	50	52	53	53	54	54	55	55
i (BIG PIGLET)	56	57	59	61	65	68	70	71	72	77	78	79	80	81	81	82	83	84	87	90	91	91	92	--	--	93
o (WATCHFUL DOG)	94	95	96	99	99	100	101	102	102	103	104	105	105	106	108	109	110	111	113	113	114	114	--	115	115	--
u / oo (DUCK AND WOODPECKER)	116	116	118	120	120	121	122	123	123	124	125	126	126	127	127	128	--	129	130	133	134	136	136	---	---	136

Block 2 — Long vowels

Sound	A	B	C	D	E	F	G	H	I	J	K	L	M	N	O	P	Q	R	S	T	U	V	W	X	Y	Z
ae (BABY SNAIL)	137	138	139	140	141	142	143	144	144	145	145	146	146	147	147	148	148	149	151	151	152	152	---	---	152	---
ee (BREEDING EAGLE)	153	154	155	155	156	157	158	159	160	161	162	162	163	164	165	165	166	167	167	169	172	173	174	175	175	---
ie (LIVELY LION)	176	177	178	178	178	180	181	182	182	183	184	184	185	186	187	187	188	189	189	190	192	192	193	194	194	---
oe (LONELY GOAT)	195	195	196	197	197	198	199	200	200	201	201	202	202	203	204	206	206	207	208	208	209	209	---	---	209	---
ue / oo (SMOOTH NEWT)	210	211	212	213	213	214	214	215	215	216	216	216	217	218	218	219	219	220	221	222	223	223	224	224	224	---

Block 3 — Long vowels

Sound	A	B	C	D	E	F	G	H	I	J	K	L	M	N	O	P	Q	R	S	T	U	V	W	X	Y	Z
ar (BASKING SHARK)	225	226	227	228	229	229	230	230	231	231	232	232	233	233	234	235	---	---	---	---	---	---	235	---	235	---
air (RARE BEAR)	236	236	236	237	238	238	239	239	239	239	239	---	---	239	240	241	241	---	---	---	---	---	---	---	---	---
er (EARLY BIRD WITH WORM)	242	243	244	245	246	247	247	248	248	249	249	249	250	249	251	252	253	254	254	255	255	---	---	---	255	---
or (WARLIKE HORSE)	256	257	258	259	260	261	261	262	263	263	263	264	265	266	267	268	268	269	---	---	---	---	---	---	269	---
oi (OYSTER-CATCHER)	270	270	270	271	271	271	272	272	272	273	273	273	273	274	274	275	275	275	275	275	---	---	---	---	---	---
ou (AN OWL SOUND)	276	276	277	278	278	279	279	279	280	280	281	282	282	283	283	284	284	---	---	---	---	---	---	---	---	---

FURTHER ACTIVITIES

Students will now be able to check and to correct the spelling of any word they want to use, and while most of the checking will be done after a draft has been produced, there should be no absolute ban on using the Dictionary in the course of writing, especially in collaborative work.

As the students are able to look up words for themselves, the teacher should stop supplying spellings on demand. After completing a piece of writing or dictation the students should mark the words they wish to look up (perhaps to a maximum fixed by the teacher). This will not only encourage students' independence, but will also save teacher time!

The more the Dictionary is used, in different subject areas, the greater will be the benefits. Whenever the teacher wants to draw new vocabulary to the attention of the group or class, the students can look the words up in the ACE Spelling Dictionary and write them up for display. Homework assignments present further opportunities for Dictionary work.

Initially, it is a good idea to set speed targets for looking up words in the Dictionary. This may be done either as a class or as a homework activity. The words may be taken from prepared lists or may be chosen by the students. If small groups work together, perhaps in competition, they will soon discover good ways of cutting down word-search time and will reach and even exceed the target of 10 words in five minutes, or 20 seconds per word. This is a realistic target for the words provided in Lessons 1–3, since these do not include words which belong in 'neutral vowel boxes'.

After mastering the basic skills of word-finding by vowel sound and first letter, students will be ready to benefit from further instruction. The section on neutral vowels, on pages IV–V of the Dictionary, should form the basis of a separate lesson. Plurals, tenses and homonyms (page VII) are also important topics to cover and to return to from time to time.

The ACE Spelling Dictionary provides a conceptual framework for understanding the complex relationships between sounds and spellings in English. Word study with the Dictionary, led by the need to communicate and to understand more about written language, is much more than a set of phonic exercises. We provide some starting points in the Activity Worksheets and hope that many more ideas for actively exploring the Dictionary will be developed by teachers and their students.

15

MORE WORD-FINDING PRACTICE

with the ACE Index and Dictionary

Aims: the student should be able to

(1) find and write down 20 page numbers from the ACE Index sheet in 5 minutes

(2) find 20 words in the ACE Dictionary in 10 minutes.

These exercises provide extra practice with the ACE Index after Lessons 1–3 in 'Learning How to Use the ACE Spelling Dictionary.' Alternatively, they can be used with the Dictionary itself to build up speed in finding words.

The teacher can work with a group or whole class using copies of the Index. The answers can be found at the back of the book.

For one-to-one or small group work, a partner or older person is needed to read out the words and to check the responses. Alternatively the exercises can be put on tape. If the topic lists are used for looking up words in the Dictionary, each student or small group will need a copy.

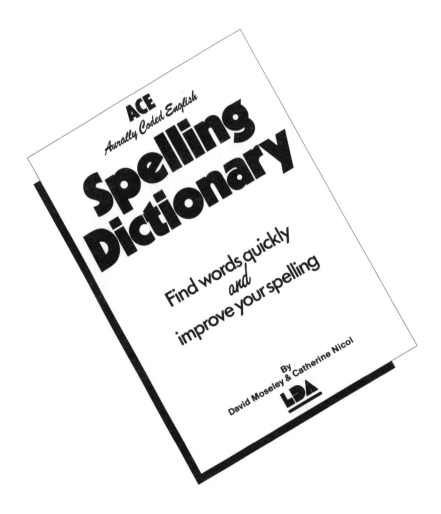

PRACTICE WITH LONG VOWEL SOUNDS
(ae) (ee) (ie) (oe) (ue)/(oo)

List of topic words to be read out or put on tape.

(a) FOOD

1. toast	6. pastry	11. sweet	16. cream ....
2. ice-cream	7. savoury	12. rice	17. loaf ....
3. roll	8. muesli..............	13. oats	18. fruit ....
4. flavour..............	9. gravy	14. soup	19. plaice ....
5. cake	10. meat..............	15. cheese.............	20. tasty..............

(b) IN THE COUNTRY

1. lake	6. stream.............	11. pool.................	16. drainage ....
2. field	7. wheat	12. rye..................	17. haystack ....
3. acorn..............	8. oak	13. tree	18. leaves ....
4. root.................	9. toadstool.........	14. flies	19. spider.............
5. stone	10. bluebells..........	15. nightingale	20. snake ....

(c) SPORT

1. team...............	6. crew	11. race	16. skiing..............
2. skating	7. rowing.............	12. climbing	17. glider ....
3. height	8. diving.............	13. player	18. bowler............
4. fielder.............	9. boot..............	14. try	19. goal ....
5. snooker	10. rival..............	15. losing	20. rules ....

(d) OCCUPATIONS

1. playwright	6. director	11. agent	16. poet..............
2. waiter	7. cleaner	12. labourer	17. dealer ....
3. salesman..........	8. librarian	13. student	18. jeweller ....
4. miner	9. grocer............	14. newsagent	19. painter ....
5. preacher..........	10. fireman...........	15. pirate..............	20. leader ....

(e) TRAVEL

1. railway	6. road..............	11. pony	16. plane ....
2. scooter............	7. bicycle	12. flight	17. cruise ....
3. breakdown........	8. timetable.........	13. train...............	18. driver ....
4. motorist...........	9. wheels............	14. pilot	19. vehicle ....
5. ocean..............	10. route	15. detour.............	20. scenery ....

The student EITHER fills in the page numbers on the sheet OR looks up the
words in the ACE Dictionary

PRACTICE WITH SHORT VOWEL SOUNDS
(a) (e) (i) (o) (u)/(oo)
List of topic words to be read out or put on tape.

© LDA ACE Spelling Activities

(a) WILDLIFE

1. butterfly ....
2. moth...................
3. squirrel ....
4. badger ....
5. fox ....
6. vixen ....
7. cub...................
8. otter.................
9. jellyfish ....
10. crab.................
11. winkle ....
12. cockle ....
13. mussel..............
14. lobster..............
15. sparrow ....
16. thrush ....
17. dove................
18. swan ....
19. kestrel ....
20. slug ....

(b) HOSPITAL

1. ambulance ....
2. bandage ....
3. injury ....
4. fracture ....
5. limb ....
6. splint ....
7. temperature .....
8. blood ....
9. vaccine............
10. stethoscope......
11. health ....
12. lung ....
13. oxygen.............
14. scalpel ....
15. unconscious ......
16. drug.................
17. tablet ....
18. pill....................
19. medication ....
20. stomach...........

(c) WINTER

1. frost ....
2. shiver ....
3. wintry ....
4. blizzard...............
5. slush ....
6. gloves ....
7. anorak ....
8. robin ....
9. Christmas.........
10. carolling ....
11. decorate............
12. presents ....
13. tinsel ....
14. glisten ....
15. holly ....
16. mistletoe ....
17. berries ....
18. sledge ....
19. pantomime.......
20. January...........

(d) HOLIDAYS

1. sand ....
2. bucket ....
3. paddle...............
4. swimming ....
5. deckchair...........
6. suntan...............
7. cottage............
8. fishing...............
9. camping ....
10. rucksack...........
11. tent ....
12. caravan............
13. disco................
14. shopping ....
15. trip...................
16. visit ....
17. exhibition..........
18. restaurant ....
19. customs.............
20. luggage ....

(e) GAMES AND PASTIMES

1. cricket...............
2. chess ....
3. golf...................
4. hockey..............
5. tennis ....
6. badminton ....
7. squash ....
8. netball ....
9. putting ....
10. jigsaws ....
11. snap ....
12. dominoes ....
13. lotto ....
14. skipping............
15. football ....
16. rugby ....
17. boxing.............
18. sledging ....
19. stilts ....
20. juggling ....

The student EITHER fills in the page numbers on the sheet OR looks up the words in the ACE Dictionary

PRACTICE WITH MIXED LONG AND SHORT

VOWEL SOUNDS ❶

List of topic words to be read out or put on tape.

(a) SCHOOL

1. cloakroom..........
2. desk.................
3. seat ....
4. teacher.............
5. subject.............
6. lesson ....
7. bell ....
8. break ....
9. snack ....
10. queue ....
11. lunch ....
12. monitor ....
13. prefect.............
14. jotter...............
15. notes ....
16. copy ....
17. science ....
18. mathematics ....
19. games.............
20. music ....

(b) DRINKS

1. coke ....
2. lemonade ....
3. milk.................
4. coffee...............
5. tea ....
6. chocolate ....
7. grapefruit ....
8. juice...............
9. wine ....
10. punch ....
11. shandy..............
12. beer ....
13. cider...............
14. scotch ....
15. whisky ....
16. brandy ....
17. alcoholic ....
18. fizzy ....
19. tonic ....
20. soda ....

(c) GUY FAWKES

1. evening.............
2. clothes ....
3. fire ....
4. wood...............
5. paper ....
6. sticks ....
7. matches..........
8. light ....
9. flame ....
10. crackle............
11. heat ....
12. bake...............
13. sausages...........
14. fireworks ....
15. colours.............
16. banger.............
17. fuse.................
18. taper...............
19. glow ....
20. embers............

(d) MOUNTAINS

1. peak.................
2. massive ....
3. rugged............
4. boulders............
5. pinnacle............
6. huge ....
7. summit ....
8. ridge ....
9. slope ....
10. avalanche........
11. precipice ....
12. sheer ....
13. edge ....
14. torrent.............
15. rocky ....
16. crag................
17. crevice............
18. trail ....
19. scramble ....
20. gully................

(e) THE RAILWAY STATION

1. ticket ....
2. office ....
3. clock ....
4. case ....
5. trolley...............
6. platform ....
7. notice ....
8. timetable.........
9. kiosk...............
10. engine ....
11. diesel...............
12. carriage............
13. train.................
14. rails.................
15. whistle.............
16. sleeper............
17. signal ....
18. buffers.............
19. bridge ....
20. taxi ....

The student EITHER fills in the page numbers on the sheet OR looks up the
words in the ACE Dictionary

19

PRACTICE WITH MIXED LONG AND SHORT
VOWEL SOUNDS 2

List of topic words to be read out or put on tape.

(a) FUN

1. smile	6. skipping	11. acting	16. chuckling
2. party	7. kissing	12. painting	17. giggling
3. happy	8. hugging	13. joke	18. merry
4. mirth	9. clown	14. tease	19. cartoon
5. joyful	10. tumbling	15. tickle	20. comic

(b) ON THE FARM

1. tractor	6. yard	11. corn	16. cattle
2. plough	7. orchard	12. barley	17. bullock
3. furrow	8. hedgerow	13. crop	18. sheep
4. fertiliser	9. harvest	14. dairy	19. goose
5. slurry	10. grain	15. herd	20. turkey

(c) WATER

1. waves	6. calm	11. whirlpool	16. trickle
2. splash	7. smooth	12. current	17. pour
3. spray	8. tranquil	13. squirt	18. still
4. choppy	9. river	14. jet	19. sparkling
5. rough	10. flow	15. fountain	20. pure

(d) FLOWERS

1. snowdrop	6. tulip	11. lily	16. foxglove
2. cowslip	7. marigold	12. lavender	17. thistle
3. hyacinth	8. pansy	13. heather	18. poppy
4. crocus	9. carnation	14. gorse	19. buttercup
5. daffodil	10. orchid	15. broom	20. daisy

(e) TREES

1. chestnut	6. birch	11. fir	16. oak
2. beech	7. ash	12. pine	17. olive
3. willow	8. palm	13. spruce	18. hazel
4. sycamore	9. holly	14. yew	19. mulberry
5. poplar	10. larch	15. bay	20. maple

The student EITHER fills in the page numbers on the sheet OR looks up the
words in the ACE Dictionary

SPELLINGS FOR SOUNDS
The sound (a) as in CAT
Spelt 'a'

Can you work out these words from the clues given? Each word contains the (a) sound. The stars tell you how many syllables are in the word.

If you like, you can use the ACE Dictionary to help you find the answers.

Check all the spellings, unless you are absolutely sure. When you have filled in the missing letters, write the whole word on the line.

If you are working with a partner, one of you can find the answers while the other writes them down.

CLUES	SYLLABLES	WRITE
e.g. good-looking	* *	h _ _ _ _ _ _ _ *handsome*
1. shaft to connect wheels	* *	ax _ _
H 2. forbidden	*	b _ _ _ _ _
3. animal of the desert	* *	c _ m _ _
4. a root vegetable	* *	c _ r _ _ _
5. a section of a book	* *	c _ _ _ t _ _
6. to become larger	* *	e _ p _ _ _
7. easily broken	* *	f _ _ g _ _ _
H 8. a French coin	*	f _ _ _ _
H 9. to take risks	* *	g _ _ b _ _
10. a suspended bed	* *	h _ m _ _ _ _
11. spoken in one or more countries	* *	l _ _ g _ _ _ _
H 12. method or way	* *	m _ n _ _ _
13. having a wife or husband	* *	m _ r _ _ _ _
H 14. a large Chinese animal	* *	p _ _ d _
15. a slight wound	*	s _ _ _ _ _ _

© **LDA** ACE Spelling Activities

H beside a word means that it is a homonym. A homonym is a word which sounds the same as or very similar to another word, but which has a different meaning. Can you find all the homonyms (or sound-alike words) from the list you have been working on?

Use the ACE Dictionary to find the homonyms you need. Remember, homonyms are marked with a star in the Dictionary and members of a pair or small group are usually quite close to each other.

When you have found all the homonyms, make up a sentence using that word and at least one other homonym: e.g. When you buy tin **tacks** you have to pay **tax**. Write out your sentences below and check the spelling of any hard words in the Dictionary.

SPELLINGS FOR SOUNDS

The sound (e) as in ELEPHANT

Spelt `ai´ `e´ `ea´ `ei´ `eo´ `ie´

Can you work out these words from the clues given? Each word contains the (e) sound. The stars tell you how many syllables are in the word.

If you like, you can use the ACE Dictionary to help you find the answers.

Check all the spellings, unless you are absolutely sure. When you have filled in the missing letters, write the whole word on the line.

If you are working with a partner, one of you can find the answers while the other writes them down.

CLUES	SYLLABLES		WRITE
e.g. an animal with spots	* *	l _ _ p _ _ _	*leopard*
1. once more	* *	ag _ _ _	_____
2. a long wooden seat	*	b _ _ _ _ _	_____
(H) 3. underground storage room	* *	c _ l _ _ _	_____
4. stockist of medicines	* *	c _ _ _ i _ _	_____
5. money owed	*	d _ _ _	_____
6. way out	* *	e _ i _	_____
7. person known and liked	*	f _ _ _ _ _	_____
(H) 8. someone who accepts an invitation	*	g _ _ _ _	_____
9. free time	* *	l _ _ s _ _ _	_____
(H) 10. what is learned	* *	l _ s _ _ _	_____
11. grassy field	* *	m _ _ d _ _	_____
(H) 12. foot lever	* *	p _ d _ _	_____
(H) 13. a liquid fuel	* *	p _ t _ _ _	_____
14. a safe haven	* *	r _ f _ _ _	_____
15. very fine cord used for sewing	*	t _ _ _ _ _	_____

H beside a word means that it is a homonym. A homonym is a word which sounds the same as or very similar to another word, but which has a different meaning. Can you find all the homonyms (or sound-alike words) from the list you have been working on?

Use the ACE Dictionary to find the homonyms you need. Remember, homonyms are marked with a star in the Dictionary and members of a pair or small group are usually quite close to each other.

When you have found all the homonyms, make up a sentence using that word and at least one other homonym: e.g. The **weather** will change **whether** we like it or not. Write out your sentences below and check the spelling of any hard words in the Dictionary.

SPELLINGS FOR SOUNDS

The sound (i) as in PIG

Spelt 'i' 'u' 'ui' 'y'

Can you work out these words from the clues given? Each word contains the (i) sound. The stars tell you how many syllables are in the word.

If you like, you can use the ACE Dictionary to help you find the answers.

Check all the spellings, unless you are absolutely sure. When you have filled in the missing letters, write the whole word on the line.

If you are working with a partner, one of you can find the answers while the other writes them down.

CLUES	SYLLABLES	WRITE
e.g. to whip with a circular motion	*	w _ _ _ _ *whisk*
1. way over a river	*	b _ _ _ _ _
H 2. to construct	*	b _ _ _ _
3. December 25th	* *	C _ _ _ _ _ m _ _
4. like clear glass	* *	c _ _ s _ _ _
5. very dirty	* *	f _ _ t _ _
H 6. a song sung in church	*	h _ _ _
7. a room in which food is cooked	* *	k _ t _ _ _ _
8. neither solid nor gas	* *	l _ q _ _ _
9. 60 seconds	* *	m _ n _ _ _
10. small hand-gun	* *	p _ _ t _ _
11. a band for tying hair	* *	r _ b _ _ _
H 12. jewellry worn on a finger	*	r _ _ _
H 13. signs which have meaning	* *	s _ _ b _ _ _
H 14. a wicked person	* *	v _ l _ _ _ _
H 15. a woman thought to use magic	*	w _ _ _ _

H beside a word means that it is a homonym. A homonym is a word which sounds the same as or very similar to another word, but which has a different meaning. Can you find all the homonyms (or sound-alike words) from the list you have been working on?

Use the ACE Dictionary to find the homonyms you need. Remember, homonyms are marked with a star in the Dictionary and members of a pair or small group are usually quite close to each other.

When you have found all the homonyms, make up a sentence using that word and at least one other homonym: e.g. The **prince** has a large collection of old **prints**. Write out your sentences below and check the spelling of any hard words in the Dictionary.

SPELLINGS FOR SOUNDS

The sound (O) as in DOG
Spelt `a` `o`

Can you work out these words from the clues given? Each word contains the (o) sound. The stars tell you how many syllables are in the word.

If you like, you can use the ACE Dictionary to help you find the answers.

Check all the spellings, unless you are absolutely sure. When you have filled in the missing letters, write the whole word on the line.

If you are working with a partner, one of you can find the answers while the other writes them down.

CLUES	SYLLABLES		WRITE
e.g. a citrus fruit	* *	or _ _ _ _	*orange*
1. an explosive device	*	b _ _ _	_____
(H) 2. to defeat in war	* *	c _ _ q _ _ _	_____
3. an intelligent sea mammal	* *	d _ _ p _ _ _	_____
4. shiny	* *	g _ _ _ _ y	_____
5. banged	*	k _ _ _ _ _ _	_____
(H) 6. a tied fastening	*	k _ _ _	_____
7. a shellfish with big claws	* *	l _ _ s _ _ _	_____
8. place of worship for Moslems	*	m _ _ _ _ _	_____
9. a book containing a long story	* *	n _ v _ _	_____
10. a fruit which yields oil	* *	ol _ _ _	_____
11. eggs beaten and fried	* *	o _ _ l _ _ _ _	_____
(H) 12. financial gain	* *	p _ _ f _ _	_____
13. a place where rocks are blasted	* *	q _ _ r _ _	_____
14. to squeeze tightly	*	s _ _ _ _ _	_____
(H) 15. unit of electric power	*	w _ _ _	_____

H beside a word means that it is a homonym. A homonym is a word which sounds the same as or very similar to another word, but which has a different meaning. Can you find all the homonyms (or sound-alike words) from the list you have been working on?

Use the ACE Dictionary to find the homonyms you need. Remember, homonyms are marked with a star in the Dictionary and members of a pair or small group are usually quite close to each other.

When you have found all the homonyms, make up a sentence using that word and at least one other homonym: e.g. The **cops** hid among the trees in the **copse**. Write out your sentences below and check the spelling of any hard words in the Dictionary.

_____

_____

_____

_____

_____

_____

_____

_____

_____

_____

_____

_____

_____

SPELLINGS FOR SOUNDS

The sound (U) as in DUCK

Spelt `o´ `o–e´ `ou´ `u´

Can you work out these words from the clues given? Each word contains the (**u**) sound. The stars tell you how many syllables are in the word.

If you like, you can use the ACE Dictionary to help you find the answers.

Check all the spellings, unless you are absolutely sure. When you have filled in the missing letters, write the whole word on the line.

If you are working with a partner, one of you can find the answers while the other writes them down.

CLUES	SYLLABLES		WRITE
e.g. very ripe and delicious	* *	l _ s _ _ _ _ _	*luscious*
1. in the middle of	* *	am _ _ _	
2. to go red with embarrassment	*	b _ _ _ _	
3. a popular caged bird	* *	b _ d _ _ _	
H 4. dried fruit, used in cakes	* *	c _ r _ _ _ _	
5. sufficient	* *	en _ _ _ _	
6. worn on the hands	*	g _ _ _ _ _	
7. cross and bad-tempered	* *	g _ _ _ p _	
8. to hurt someone's pride	* *	i _ s _ _ _	
H 9. a soft, purple fruit	*	p _ _ _	
H 10. a woman living in a convent	*	n _ _	
11. stuff to be thrown away	* *	r _ b _ _ _ _	
H 12. bones protecting the brain	*	s _ _ _ _	
H 13. a certain number or amount	*	s _ _ _	
14. unwanted problems	* *	t _ _ _ b _ _ _	
15. to the floor above	* *	u _ s _ _ _ _ _	

H beside a word means that it is a homonym. A homonym is a word which sounds the same as or very similar to another word, but which has a different meaning. Can you find all the homonyms (or sound-alike words) from the list you have been working on?

Use the ACE Dictionary to find the homonyms you need. Remember, homonyms are marked with a star in the Dictionary and members of a pair or small group are usually quite close to each other.

When you have found all the homonyms, make up a sentence using that word and at least one other homonym: e.g. She was the **one** who **won** a holiday. Write out your sentences below and check the spelling of any hard words in the Dictionary.

SPELLINGS FOR SOUNDS

The sound (ae) as in SNAIL

Spelt `a´ `a–e´ `ai´ `ay´ `ea´ `ei´

Can you work out these words from the clues given? Each word contains the (**ae**) sound. The stars tell you how many syllables are in the word.

If you like, you can use the ACE Dictionary to help you find the answers.

Check all the spellings, unless you are absolutely sure. When you have filled in the missing letters, write the whole word on the line.

If you are working with a partner, one of you can find the answers while the other writes them down.

CLUES	SYLLABLES		WRITE
e.g. a flatfish	*	p _ _ _ _ _	*plaice*
1. a continuing pain	*	a _ _ _	_____
2. very old indeed	* *	a _ c _ _ _ _	_____
(H) 3. to smash into pieces	*	b _ _ _ _	_____
4. a baby's bed	* *	c _ _ d _ _	_____
5. to breathe out	* *	e _ h _ _ _	_____
6. well-known	* *	f _ m _ _ _	_____
(H) 7. a way of walking	*	g _ _ _	_____
(H) 8. rub into small pieces	*	g _ _ _ _	_____
9. misty	* *	h _ z _	_____
10. prison	*	j _ _ _	_____
(H) 11. put down in one place	*	l _ _ _	_____
(H) 12. letters and parcels	*	m _ _ _	_____
13. an error	* *	m _ _ t _ _ _	_____
(H) 14. a board for carrying things	*	t _ _ _	_____
(H) 15. heaviness	*	w _ _ _ _ _	_____

H beside a word means that it is a homonym. A homonym is a word which sounds the same as or very similar to another word, but which has a different meaning. Can you find all the homonyms (or sound-alike words) from the list you have been working on?

Use the ACE Dictionary to find the homonyms you need. Remember, homonyms are marked with a star in the Dictionary and members of a pair or small group are usually quite close to each other.

When you have found all the homonyms, make up a sentence using that word and at least one other homonym: e.g. Will **plaice** do in **place** of cod? Write out your sentences below and check the spelling of any hard words in the Dictionary.

_____

_____

_____

_____

_____

_____

_____

_____

_____

_____

_____

_____

_____

_____

_____

_____

SPELLINGS FOR SOUNDS

The sound (ee) as in EAGLE

Spelt `e´ `ea´ `ee´ `ei´ `ey´

Can you work out these words from the clues given? Each word contains the (**ee**) sound. The stars tell you how many syllables are in the word.

If you like, you can use the ACE Dictionary to help you find the answers.

Check all the spellings, unless you are absolutely sure. When you have filled in the missing letters, write the whole word on the line.

If you are working with a partner, one of you can find the answers while the other writes them down.

CLUES	SYLLABLES		WRITE
e.g. trousers made out of denim	*	j _ _ _ _	*jeans*
1. to come into view	* *	ap _ _ _ _ _	
2. hard-backed insect	* *	b _ _ t _ _	
H 3. a squeaking noise	*	c _ _ _ _	
H 4. an animal found in forests	*	d _ _ _	
5. to mislead with lies	* *	d _ c _ _ _ _ _	
6. keen and enthusiastic	* *	e _ g _ _	
7. having the same value	* *	eq _ _ _	
8. occurring often	* *	f _ _ q _ _ _ _	
9. opening in a lock	* *	k _ _ h _ _ _	
H 10. rented	*	l _ _ _ _ _	
H 11. measuring machine	* *	m _ t _ _	
12. small tool used for sewing	* *	n _ _ d _ _	
H 13. period without war	*	p _ _ _ _	
14. feeling sick	* *	q _ _ _ s _	
15. grab hold of	*	s _ _ _ _	

H beside a word means that it is a homonym. A homonym is a word which sounds the same as or very similar to another word, but which has a different meaning. Can you find all the homonyms (or sound-alike words) from the list you have been working on?

Use the ACE Dictionary to find the homonyms you need. Remember, homonyms are marked with a star in the Dictionary and members of a pair or small group are usually quite close to each other.

When you have found all the homonyms, make up a sentence using that word and at least one other homonym: e.g. It is not easy to **steal** a safe made of **steel**. Write out your sentences below and check the spelling of any hard words in the Dictionary.

SPELLINGS FOR SOUNDS

The sound (ie) as in LION

Spelt 'i' 'i–e' 'igh' 'uy' 'y' 'ye'

Can you work out these words from the clues given? Each word contains the (**ie**) sound. The stars tell you how many syllables are in the word.

If you like, you can use the ACE Dictionary to help you find the answers.

Check all the spellings, unless you are absolutely sure. When you have filled in the missing letters, write the whole word on the line.

If you are working with a partner, one of you can find the answers while the other writes them down.

CLUES	SYLLABLES		WRITE
e.g. an absence of sound	* *	s _ l _ _ _ _	*silence*
1. muscles in the arm	* *	b _ c _ _ _	_____
(H) 2. gear for controlling a horse	* *	b _ _ d _ _	_____
(H) 3. someone who makes a purchase	* *	b _ y _ _	_____
4. a person riding a bicycle	* *	c _ c _ _ _ _	_____
5. to weaken a solution	* *	d _ l _ _ _	_____
(H) 6. coloured liquid for staining	*	d _ _	_____
7. to ask	* *	e _ q _ _ _ _	_____
8. good advice	* *	g _ _ d _ _ _ _	_____
(H) 9. an image that is worshipped	* *	id _ _	_____
(H) 10. an electric flash in the sky	* *	l _ _ _ _ n _ _ _	_____
(H) 11. may, perhaps	*	m _ _ _ _	_____
12. tall metal support for cables	* *	p _ l _ _	_____
13. the rise and fall of the sea	*	t _ d _	_____
(H) 14. make weary	*	t _ _ _	_____
15. to shake rapidly	* *	v _ b _ _ _ _	_____

35

H beside a word means that it is a homonym. A homonym is a word which sounds the same as or very similar to another word, but which has a different meaning. Can you find all the homonyms (or sound-alike words) from the list you have been working on?

Use the ACE Dictionary to find the homonyms you need. Remember, homonyms are marked with a star in the Dictionary and members of a pair or small group are usually quite close to each other.

When you have found all the homonyms, make up a sentence using that word and at least one other homonym: e.g. If the cost is **higher** we won't **hire** it. Write out your sentences below and check the spelling of any hard words in the Dictionary.

_____

_____

_____

_____

_____

_____

_____

_____

_____

_____

_____

_____

_____

SPELLINGS FOR SOUNDS

The sound (oe) as in LONELY GOAT

Spelt `o´ `oa´ `o–e´ `ough´ `ow´

Can you work out these words from the clues given? Each word contains the (**oe**) sound. The stars tell you how many syllables are in the word.

If you like, you can use the ACE Dictionary to help you find the answers.

Check all the spellings, unless you are absolutely sure. When you have filled in the missing letters, write the whole word on the line.

If you are working with a partner, one of you can find the answers while the other writes them down.

CLUES	SYLLABLES		WRITE
e.g. comfy and warm	* *	c _ s _	cosy
H 1. brave and courageous	*	b _ _ _	_____
2. a burglar may use this tool	* *	c _ _ _ b _ _	_____
H 3. flour and water mixed together	*	d _ _ _ _	_____
4. made solid by the cold	* *	f _ _ z _ _	_____
5. to shine in the dark	*	g _ _ _	_____
6. an adult	* *	g _ _ _ _ _ - u _	_____
H 7. something lent	*	l _ _ _	_____
8. to complain or groan in pain	*	m _ _ _	_____
9. an enormous area of sea	* *	o _ _ _ _ _	_____
10. to cook gently in water	*	p _ _ _ _ _	_____
H 11. lines of things	*	r _ _ _	_____
12. a white winter flower	* *	s _ _ _ d _ _ _	_____
H 13. under-part of the foot	*	s _ _ _	_____
14. a monarch's chair	*	t _ _ _ _ _	_____
H 15. the yellow part of an egg	*	y _ _ _	_____

© **LDA** ACE Spelling Activities

H beside a word means that it is a homonym. A homonym is a word which sounds the same as or very similar to another word, but which has a different meaning. Can you find all the homonyms (or sound-alike words) from the list you have been working on?

Use the ACE Dictionary to find the homonyms you need. Remember, homonyms are marked with a star in the Dictionary and members of a pair or small group are usually quite close to each other.

When you have found all the homonyms, make up a sentence using that word and at least one other homonym: e.g. The **whole** class helped to dig the **hole**. Write out your sentences below and check the spelling of any hard words in the Dictionary.

_____

_____

_____

_____

_____

_____

_____

_____

_____

_____

_____

_____

_____

SPELLINGS FOR SOUNDS

The sound (oo) or (ue) as in SMOOTH NEWT

Spelt 'eau' 'eu' 'ew' 'oo' 'u' 'u–e' 'ui'

Can you work out these words from the clues given? Each word contains the (**oo**) or (**ue**) sound. The stars tell you how many syllables are in the word.

If you like, you can use the ACE Dictionary to help you find the answers.

Check all the spellings, unless you are absolutely sure. When you have filled in the missing letters, write the whole word on the line.

If you are working with a partner, one of you can find the answers while the other writes them down.

CLUES	SYLLABLES	WRITE
e.g. travel bag for clothes	* *	s _ _ _ c _ _ _ *suitcase*
1. to cause laughter or fun	* *	am _ _ _
2. great attractiveness	* *	b _ _ _ _ _
H 3. a dark-coloured injury	*	b _ _ _ _ _
H 4. to select	*	c _ _ _ _ _
H 5. to holiday on a boat	*	c _ _ _ _ _
H 6. morning wetness on the grass	*	d _ _
7. a continent	* *	E _ _ _ _ _
8. depressed, cheerless	* *	g _ _ _ _ _
9. the feet of horses or goats	*	h _ _ _ _ _
10. a liquid from fruit	*	j _ _ _ _
H 11. recently made or obtained	*	n _ _
12. a pest, something annoying	* *	n _ _ s _ _ _ _
13. to damage with chemicals	* *	p _ ll _ _ _
14. red stems made into pies	* *	r _ _ b _ _ _
H 15. to fire with a gun	*	s _ _ _ _

39

H beside a word means that it is a homonym. A homonym is a word which sounds the same as or very similar to another word, but which has a different meaning. Can you find all the homonyms (or sound-alike words) from the list you have been working on?

Use the ACE Dictionary to find the homonyms you need. Remember, homonyms are marked with a star in the Dictionary and members of a pair or small group are usually quite close to each other.

When you have found all the homonyms, make up a sentence using that word and at least one other homonym: e.g. He joined the **queue** for a free snooker **cue**. Write out your sentences below and check the spelling of any hard words in the Dictionary.

_____

_____

_____

_____

_____

_____

_____

_____

_____

_____

_____

_____

_____

_____

SPELLINGS FOR SOUNDS

The sound (ar) as in SHARK

Spelt 'a' 'ar' 'arrh' 'ear' 'er'

Can you work out these words from the clues given? Each word contains the (**ar**) sound. The stars tell you how many syllables are in the word.

If you like, you can use the ACE Dictionary to help you find the answers.

Check all the spellings, unless you are absolutely sure. When you have filled in the missing letters, write the whole word on the line.

If you are working with a partner, one of you can find the answers while the other writes them down.

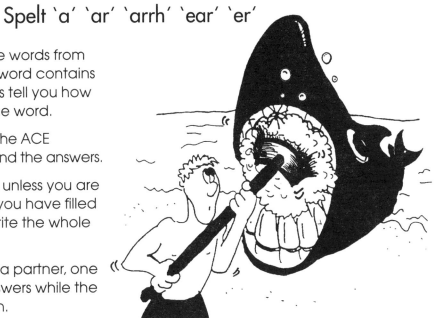

CLUES	SYLLABLES		WRITE
e.g. a good buy	* *	b _ _ g _ _ _	*bargain*
1. part of a circle	*	a _ _	_____
2. a grain crop	* *	b _ _ l _ _	_____
3. a floor covering	* *	c _ _ p _ _	_____
4. a cardboard container	* *	c _ _ t _ _	_____
5. mucus in the nose and throat	* *	c _ t _ _ _ _	_____
6. a greater distance	* *	f _ _ t _ _ _	_____
7. stringed musical instrument	* *	g _ _ t _ _	_____
8. spear for hunting fish	* *	h _ _ p _ _ _	_____
9. time to gather in crops	* *	h _ _ v _ _ _	_____
10. organ that pumps blood	*	h _ _ _ _	_____
11. a light beer	* *	l _ g _ _	_____
12. a packet	* *	p _ _ c _ _	_____
13. worn round the neck	*	s _ _ _ _	_____
14. rank in army	* *	s _ _ g _ _ _ _	_____
15. a clear paint	* *	v _ _ n _ _ _	_____

Clues 1, 6, and 10 are marked with an **H**.

41

© LDA ACE Spelling Activities

H beside a word means that it is a homonym. A homonym is a word which sounds the same as or very similar to another word, but which has a different meaning. Can you find all the homonyms (or sound-alike words) from the list you have been working on?

Use the ACE Dictionary to find the homonyms you need. Remember, homonyms are marked with a star in the Dictionary and members of a pair or small group are usually quite close to each other.

When you have found all the homonyms, make up a sentence using that word and at least one other homonym: e.g. We **aren't** going to stay with our **aunt**. Write out your sentences below and check the spelling of any hard words in the Dictionary.

_____

_____

_____

_____

_____

_____

_____

_____

_____

_____

_____

_____

_____

_____

_____

SPELLINGS FOR SOUNDS

The sound (air) as in BEAR

Spelt `a` `air` `are` `ere`

Can you work out these words from the clues given? Each word contains the (**air**) sound. The stars tell you how many syllables are in the word.

If you like, you can use the ACE Dictionary to help you find the answers.

Check all the spellings, unless you are absolutely sure. When you have filled in the missing letters, write the whole word on the line.

If you are working with a partner, one of you can find the answers while the other writes them down.

CLUES	SYLLABLES		WRITE
e.g. make-believe little folk	* *	f _ _ _ _ _ _	*fairies*
1. conscious	* *	aw _ _ _	_____
2. uncovered	*	b _ _ _	_____
3. hardly	* *	b _ _ _ l _	_____
4. slipshod	* *	c _ _ _ l _ _ _	_____
5. bravely taking risks	* *	d _ r _ _ _	_____
6. charge for a ride	*	f _ _ _	_____
7. goodbye	* *	f _ _ _ w _ _ _	_____
8. animal like a rabbit	*	h _ _ _	_____
9. mother or father	* *	p _ r _ _ _	_____
10. get ready	* *	p _ _ p _ _ _	_____
11. mend	* *	r _ p _ _ _	_____
12. frightening	* *	s _ _ r _	_____
13. look with fixed gaze	*	s _ _ _ _	_____
14. to or in that place	*	t _ _ _ _	_____
15. to or in what place	*	w _ _ _ _	_____

43

H beside a word means that it is a homonym. A homonym is a word which sounds the same as or very similar to another word, but which has a different meaning. Can you find all the homonyms (or sound-alike words) from the list you have been working on?

Use the ACE Dictionary to find the homonyms you need. Remember, homonyms are marked with a star in the Dictionary and members of a pair or small group are usually quite close to each other.

When you have found all the homonyms, make up a sentence using that word and at least one other homonym: e.g. The **mayor** rode on a grey **mare**. Write out your sentences below and check the spelling of any hard words in the Dictionary.

_____

_____

_____

_____

_____

_____

_____

_____

_____

_____

_____

_____

_____

_____

SPELLINGS FOR SOUNDS

The sound (er) as in BIRD

Spelt 'ear' 'er' 'ir' 'ol' 'or' 'our' 'ur'

Can you work out these words from the clues given? Each word contains the (**er**) sound. The stars tell you how many syllables are in the word.

If you like, you can use the ACE Dictionary to help you find the answers.

Check all the spellings, unless you are absolutely sure. When you have filled in the missing letters, write the whole word on the line.

If you are working with a partner, one of you can find the answers while the other writes them down.

CLUES	SYLLABLES		WRITE
e.g. easily frightened	* *	n _ _ v _ _ _	*nervous*
1. ridiculous	* *	a _ s _ _ _	_____
2. on the look-out	* *	a l _ _ _	_____
H 3. delivery of a baby	*	b _ _ _ _	_____
4. thief who breaks in	* *	b _ _ g _ _ _	_____
H 5. army officer	* *	c _ _ _ n _ _	_____
6. not clean	* *	d _ _ t _	_____
H 7. to obtain money from work	*	e _ _ _	_____
H 8. coat of an animal	*	f _ _	_____
9. to make a bubbling sound	* *	g _ _ g _ _	_____
10. a daily record or paper	* *	j _ _ _ n _ _	_____
11. kill	* *	m _ _ d _ _	_____
12. speak in a low voice	* *	m _ _ m _ _	_____
13. scent	* *	p _ _ f _ _ _	_____
14. to buy	* *	p _ _ c _ _ _ _	_____
H 15. the earth	*	w _ _ _ _	_____

H beside a word means that it is a homonym. A homonym is a word which sounds the same as or very similar to another word, but which has a different meaning. Can you find all the homonyms (or sound-alike words) from the list you have been working on?

Use the ACE Dictionary to find the homonyms you need. Remember, homonyms are marked with a star in the Dictionary and members of a pair or small group are usually quite close to each other.

When you have found all the homonyms, make up a sentence using that word and at least one other homonym: e.g. We took **turns** to look through the binoculars at the **terns**. Write out your sentences below and check the spelling of any hard words in the Dictionary.

SPELLINGS FOR SOUNDS

The sound (or) as in HORSE

Spelt 'al' 'ar' 'au' 'augh' 'aw' 'oar' 'ore' 'or' 'our'

Can you work out these words from the clues given? Each word contains the (**or**) sound. The stars tell you how many syllables are in the word.

If you like, you can use the ACE Dictionary to help you find the answers.

Check all the spellings, unless you are absolutely sure. When you have filled in the missing letters, write the whole word on the line.

If you are working with a partner, one of you can find the answers while the other writes them down.

CLUES	SYLLABLES	WRITE
e.g. an animal you can ride	*	h _ _ _ _ *horse*
1. dreadful	* *	a _ f _ _
2. a plank	*	b _ _ _ _
3. a girl child	* *	d _ _ _ _ t _ _
4. strength or power	*	f _ _ _ _
5. wealth, good luck	* *	f _ _ t _ _ _
6. splendid and attractive	* *	g _ _ g _ _ _ _
7. to visit as a ghost	*	h _ _ _ _
8. a bird of prey	*	h _ _ _
9. a period of grief after loss	* *	m _ _ _ _ i _ _
10. mischievous and disobedient	* *	n _ _ _ _ t _
11. cup and _ _ _ _ _ _	* *	s _ _ c _ _
12. beach	*	s _ _ _ _
13. stem	*	s _ _ _ _
14. to go somewhere on foot	*	w _ _ _
15. prolonged fighting	*	w _ _

(H) 2. a plank
(H) 9. a period of grief after loss
(H) 12. beach
(H) 13. stem
(H) 15. prolonged fighting

H beside a word means that it is a homonym. A homonym is a word which sounds the same as or very similar to another word, but which has a different meaning. Can you find all the homonyms (or sound-alike words) from the list you have been working on?

Use the ACE Dictionary to find the homonyms you need. Remember, homonyms are marked with a star in the Dictionary and members of a pair or small group are usually quite close to each other.

When you have found all the homonyms, make up a sentence using that word and at least one other homonym: e.g. They **fought** hard to capture the **fort**. Write out your sentences below and check the spelling of any hard words in the Dictionary.

SPELLINGS FOR SOUNDS

The sound (oi) as in OYSTER-CATCHER

Spelt `oi´ `oy´ `uoy´

Can you work out these words from the clues given? Each word contains the (**oi**) sound. The stars tell you how many syllables are in the word.

If you like, you can use the ACE Dictionary to help you find the answers.

Check all the spellings, unless you are absolutely sure. When you have filled in the missing letters, write the whole word on the line.

If you are working with a partner, one of you can find the answers while the other writes them down.

CLUES	SYLLABLES		WRITE
e.g. unpleasant loud sound	*	n _ _ _ _	*noise*
1. keep away from	* *	av _ _ _	_____
2. bubbling hot	* *	b _ _ l _ _ _	_____
H 3. floating marker	*	b _ _ _	_____
4. what you choose	*	c _ _ _ _ _	_____
H 5. money	*	c _ _ _	_____
6. take on for work	* *	e _ p _ _ _	_____
7. a large entrance hall	* *	f _ _ e _	_____
8. to heave up	*	h _ _ _ _	_____
9. full of happiness	* *	j _ _ f _ _	_____
10. soothing cream	* *	o _ _ _ m _ _ _	_____
11. shellfish in which pearls grow	* *	o _ s _ _ _	_____
12. kill with a deadly substance	* *	p _ _ s _ _	_____
13. show great happiness	* *	r _ j _ _ _ _	_____
14. made dirty	*	s _ _ _ _ _	_____
15. hard work	*	t _ _ _	_____

H beside a word means that it is a homonym. A homonym is a word which sounds the same as or very similar to another word, but which has a different meaning. Can you find all the homonyms (or sound-alike words) from the list you have been working on?

Use the ACE Dictionary to find the homonyms you need. Remember, homonyms are marked with a star in the Dictionary and members of a pair or small group are usually quite close to each other.

When you have found all the homonyms, make up a sentence using that word and at least one other homonym: e.g. I hurt my **groin** when I tried to leap over the **groyne**. Write out your sentences below and check the spelling of any hard words in the Dictionary.

_____

_____

_____

_____

_____

_____

_____

_____

_____

_____

_____

_____

_____

SPELLINGS FOR SOUNDS

The sound (OU) as in OWL

Spelt 'ou' 'ough' 'ow'

Can you work out these words from the clues given? Each word contains the (**ou**) sound. The stars tell you how many syllables are in the word.

If you like, you can use the ACE Dictionary to help you find the answers.

Check all the spellings, unless you are absolutely sure. When you have filled in the missing letters, write the whole word on the line.

If you are working with a partner, one of you can find the answers while the other writes them down.

CLUES	SYLLABLES		WRITE
e.g. a small animal with a long tail	*	m _ _ _ _	*mouse*
H 1. permitted	* *	all _ _ _ _	_____
H 2. a branch	*	b _ _ _ _	_____
H 3. a person who lacks courage	* *	c _ _ a _ _	_____
4. a large group of people	*	c _ _ _ _	_____
5. almost falling asleep	* *	d _ _ _ s _	_____
H 6. blossom	* *	f _ _ _ _ _	_____
H 7. disgusting	*	f _ _ _	_____
H 8. period of time	*	h _ _ _	_____
9. part of the face	*	m _ _ _ _	_____
10. dig up into furrows	*	p _ _ _ _ _	_____
11. a game with bat and ball	* *	r _ _ _ d _ _ _	_____
12. noisy and badly behaved	* *	r _ _ d _	_____
13. start to grow	*	s _ _ _ _ _	_____
14. 10 × 100	* *	t _ _ _ s _ _ _	_____
15. a garden tool	* (*)	t _ _ _ _ _	_____

H beside a word means that it is a homonym. A homonym is a word which sounds the same as or very similar to another word, but which has a different meaning. Can you find all the homonyms (or sound-alike words) from the list you have been working on?

Use the ACE Dictionary to find the homonyms you need. Remember, homonyms are marked with a star in the Dictionary and members of a pair or small group are usually quite close to each other.

When you have found all the homonyms, make up a sentence using that word and at least one other homonym: e.g. I advise and **counsel** you to stand for the **council**. Write out your sentences below and check the spelling of any hard words in the Dictionary.

_____

_____

_____

_____

_____

_____

_____

_____

_____

_____

_____

_____

SPELLING FOR SOUND PUZZLES

The sound (ae) as in SNAIL

Can you follow the lines below to join the beginnings and endings of the words to the middle sound (**ae**)?

Remember that the sound (**ae**) will be spelt in different ways, so check the words in the ACE Spelling Dictionary before you write them down.

When you have found all seven words, you can use them to fill in the crossword puzzle.

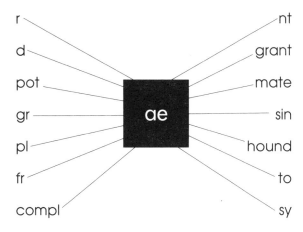

r — nt
d — grant
pot — mate
gr — ae — sin
pl — hound
fr — to
compl — sy

_____

_____

_____

_____

_____

_____

_____

CLUES

1. a criticism
2. a racing dog
3. a dried grape
4. a friend to have fun with
5. sweet-smelling
6. a vegetable grown in the ground
7. a common flower

SPELLING FOR SOUND PUZZLES

The sound (ee) as in EAGLE

Can you follow the lines below to join the beginnings and endings of the words to the middle sound (**ee**)?

Remember that the sound (**ee**) will be spelt in different ways, so check the words in the ACE Spelling Dictionary before you write them down.

When you have found all seven words, you can use them to fill in the crossword puzzle.

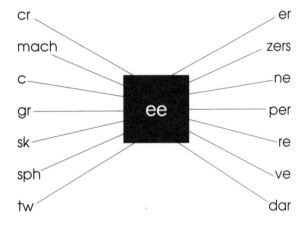

cr   er

mach   zers

c   ne

gr   **ee**   per

sk   re

sph   ve

tw   dar

_____

_____

_____

_____

_____

_____

_____

CLUES

1. show deep sadness

2. a solid circular shape

3. an instrument for plucking hairs

4. a mechanical device

5. a climbing plant

6. an evergreen tree

7. a person gliding on snow

SPELLING FOR SOUND PUZZLES
The sound (ie) as in LION

Can you follow the lines below to join the beginnings and endings of the words to the middle sound (**ie**)?

Remember that the sound (**ie**) will be spelt in different ways, so check the words in the ACE Spelling Dictionary before you write them down.

When you have found all seven words, you can use them to fill in the crossword puzzle.

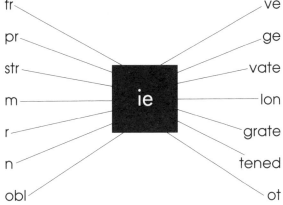

fr
pr
str
m
r
n
obl

ie

ve
ge
vate
lon
grate
tened
ot

_____

_____

_____

_____

_____

_____

_____

CLUES

1. to work hard to reach an aim

2. afraid

3. to do a favour for someone

4. not public

5. a revolt

6. a fabric used for making stockings

7. go to live in another country

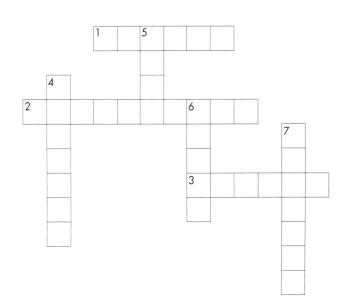

© **LDA** ACE Spelling Activities

SPELLING FOR SOUND PUZZLES

The sound (oe) as in GOAT

Can you follow the lines below to join the beginnings and endings of the words to the middle sound (**oe**)?

Remember that the sound (**oe**) will be spelt in different ways, so check the words in the ACE Spelling Dictionary before you write them down.

When you have found all seven words, you can use them to fill in the crossword puzzle.

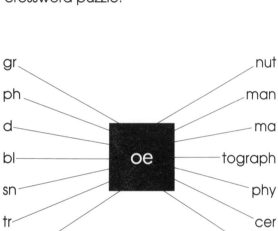

gr   nut
ph   man
d   ma
bl   **oe**   tograph
sn   phy
tr   cer
dipl   lamp

_____

CLUES

1. round cake with a hole

2. figure who melts

3. certificate

4. shopkeeper selling food

5. gadget making a hot flame

6. image printed from film

7. prize

SPELLING FOR SOUND PUZZLES

The sound (oo) or (ue) as in SMOOTH NEWT

Can you follow the lines below to join the beginnings and endings of the words to the middle sound (**oo/ue**)?

Remember that the sounds (**oo**) and (**ue**) will be spelt in different ways, so check the words in the ACE Spelling Dictionary before you write them down.

When you have found all seven words, you can use them to fill in the crossword puzzle.

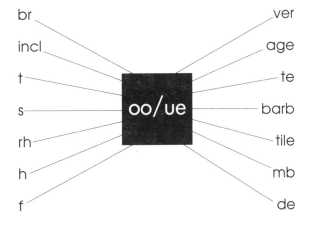

br   ver
incl   age
t   te
s   oo/ue   barb
rh   tile
h   mb
f   de

_____
_____
_____
_____
_____
_____
_____

CLUES

1. cleaning machine

2. burial chamber

3. a cruel person

4. put in a group

5. useless

6. plant with pink stems, used for pies

7. human waste

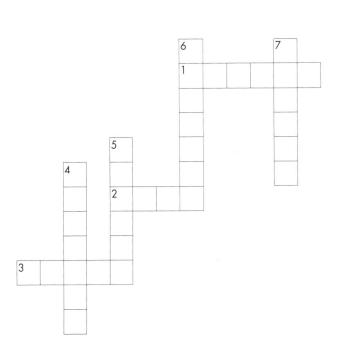

© **LDA** ACE Spelling Activities

SPELLING FOR SOUND PUZZLES

The sound (ar) as in SHARK

Can you follow the lines below to join the beginnings and endings of the words to the middle sound (**ar**)?

Remember that the sound (**ar**) will be spelt in different ways, so check the words in the ACE Spelling Dictionary before you write them down.

When you have found all seven words, you can use them to fill in the crossword puzzle.

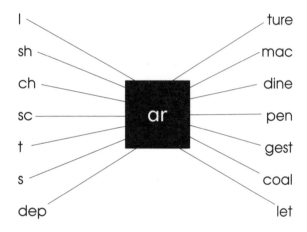

l	ture
sh	mac
ch	dine
sc	pen
t	gest
s	coal
dep	let

_____

_____

_____

_____

_____

_____

_____

CLUES

1. a tinned fish

2. make into a point

3. charred wood

4. biggest

5. setting off on a journey

6. bright red

7. used for road surfaces

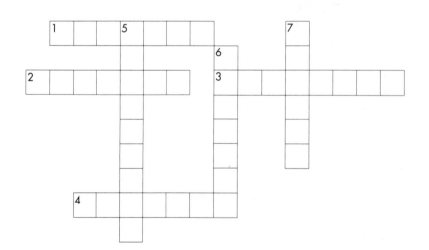

SPELLING FOR SOUND PUZZLES

The sound (air) as in BEAR

Can you follow the lines below to join the beginnings and endings of the words to the middle sound (**air**)?

Remember that the sound (**air**) will be spelt in different ways, so check the words in the ACE Spelling Dictionary before you write them down.

When you have found all seven words, you can use them to fill in the crossword puzzle.

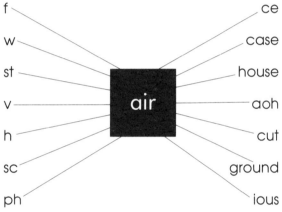

f
w
st
v
h
sc
ph

air

ce
case
house
aoh
cut
ground
ious

_____

_____

_____

_____

_____

_____

_____

CLUES

1. of different kinds

2. ruler of ancient Egypt

3. in short supply

4. a barber's handiwork

5. building for storing goods

6. steps from floor to floor

7. amusement park

SPELLING FOR SOUND PUZZLES

The sound (er) as in BIRD

Can you follow the lines below to join the beginnings and endings of the words to the middle sound (**er**)?

Remember that the sound (**er**) will be spelt in different ways, so check the words in the ACE Spelling Dictionary before you write them down.

When you have found all seven words, you can use them to fill in the crossword puzzle.

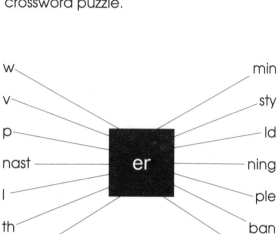

w
v
p
nast
l
th
sub

er

min
sty
ld
ning
ple
ban
tium

_____
_____
_____
_____
_____
_____
_____

CLUES

1. rats, mice and other pests

2. of the outer city

3. the globe we live on

4. a royal colour

5. needing a drink

6. an orange trumpet-shaped flower

7. gaining knowledge or skill

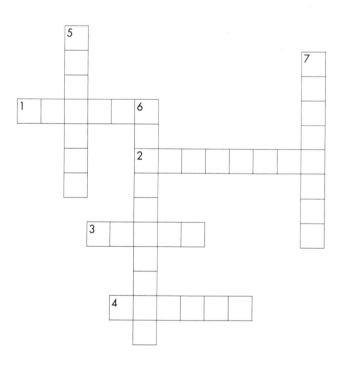

SPELLING FOR SOUND PUZZLES

The sound (or) as in HORSE

Can you follow the lines below to join the beginnings and endings of the words to the middle sound (**or**)?

Remember that the sound (**or**) will be spelt in different ways, so check the words in the ACE Spelling Dictionary before you write them down.

When you have found all seven words, you can use them to fill in the crossword puzzle.

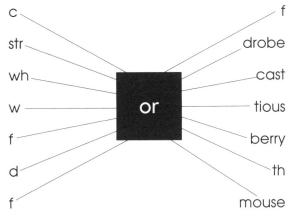

c

str

wh

w

f

d

f

or

f

drobe

cast

tious

berry

th

mouse

_____
_____
_____
_____
_____
_____
_____

CLUES

1. a place where ships unload

2. after third and before fifth

3. a soft red fruit

4. a cupboard for clothes

5. nervous and careful

6. a prediction

7. a small, sleepy country creature

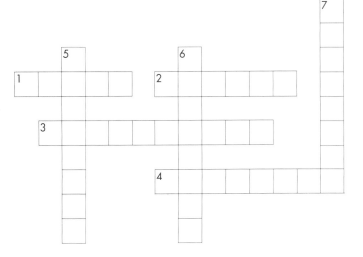

© **LDA** ACE Spelling Activities

SPELLING FOR SOUND PUZZLES

The sound (oi) as in OYSTER-CATCHER

Can you follow the lines below to join the beginnings and endings of the words to the middle sound (**oi**)?

Remember that the sound (**oi**) will be spelt in different ways, so check the words in the ACE Spelling Dictionary before you write them down.

When you have found all seven words, you can use them to fill in the crossword puzzle.

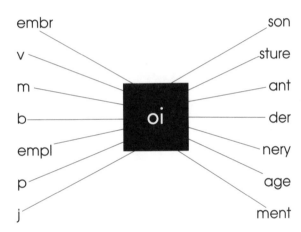

embr   son
v   sture
m   ant
b   oi   der
empl   nery
p   age
j   ment

_____

_____

_____

_____

_____

_____

_____

CLUES

1. carpentry on a small scale

2. able to float easily

3. deadly substance

4. situation with pay

5. dampness

6. decorate with stitches

7. sea journey

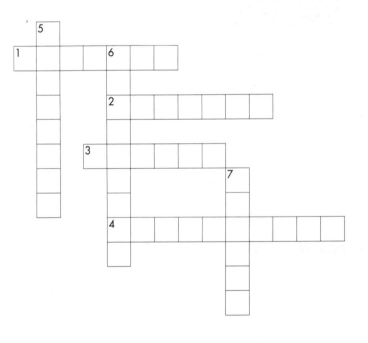

SPELLING FOR SOUND PUZZLES

The sound (OU) as in OWL

Can you follow the lines below to join the beginnings and endings of the words to the middle sound (**ou**)?

Remember that the sound (**ou**) will be spelt in different ways, so check the words in the ACE Spelling Dictionary before you write them down.

When you have found all seven words, you can use them to fill in the crossword puzzle.

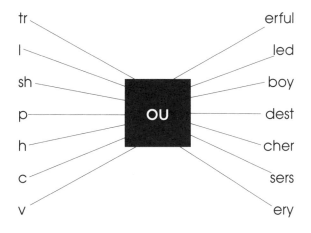

tr		erful
l		led
sh		boy
p	**OU**	dest
h		cher
c		sers
v		ery

_____

_____

_____

_____

_____

_____

_____

CLUES

1. herder of cattle

2. full of strength

3. rainy

4. a ticket worth money

5. garment worn on legs

6. cried like a wolf

7. noisiest

CAR REGISTRATION GAME ①

Find words which include these car registration letters. The first letter must be the first letter in the word and the last letter the last letter of the word. You are also given an ACE vowel sound which is included in the word, but you are not told how that sound is spelt.

You will be able to find all the answers in the ACE Dictionary if you turn to the right page. As you know the vowel sound and the first letter, you can use the Index. All the words have two syllables (**).

CLUES	e.g. JKY	ⓞ	– page 103 –	*jockey*

	CLUES			
1.	HVY	ⓔ		_ _ _ _ _
2.	BCN	ⓐⓔ		_ _ _ _ _
3.	BDY	ⓞ		_ _ _ _
4.	RWD	ⓞⓡ		_ _ _ _ _ _
5.	WMN	ⓞⓞ		_ _ _ _ _
6.	BLT	ⓐⓔ		_ _ _ _ _ _ _ _
7.	RPN	ⓘⓔ		_ _ _ _ _
8.	SCT	ⓔⓔ		_ _ _ _ _ _

Now complete the puzzle, using the 8 words that you have made.

CLUES

1. a breakfast food

2. a female person

3. a prize

4. a piece of jewellry

5. the frame of a person or animal

6. hard to lift

7. something hidden or unrevealed

8. to grow towards perfection, as fruit does

CAR REGISTRATION GAME ②

Find words which include these car registration letters. The first letter must be the first letter in the word and the last letter the last letter of the word. You are also given an ACE vowel sound which is included in the word, but you are not told how that sound is spelt.

You will be able to find all the answers in the ACE Dictionary if you turn to the right page. As you know the vowel sound and the first letter, you can use the Index. All the words have two syllables (**).

CLUES	e.g. CBY	ou	– page 277 –	cowboy

1.	KTP	e		_ _ _ _ _ _
2.	NHL	ie		_ _ _ _ _ _ _ _
3.	OTH	o		_ _ _ _ _ _
4.	EHT	or		_ _ _ _ _ _
5.	FSN	a		_ _ _ _ _ _
6.	WPL	er		_ _ _ _ _ _ _ _
7.	RSN	ee		_ _ _ _ _
8.	WKT	i		_ _ _ _ _

Now complete the puzzle, using the 8 words that you have made.

CLUES

1. swirling water

2. fumes from a car

3. a long-legged bird

4. dusk followed by darkness

5. sauce

6. a popular style

7. an explanation for something

8. a target you bowl at in cricket

65

CAR REGISTRATION GAME

Find words which include these car registration letters. The first letter must be the first letter in the word and the last letter the last letter of the word. You are also given an ACE vowel sound which is included in the word, but you are not told how that sound is spelt.

You will be able to find all the answers in the ACE Dictionary if you turn to the right page. As you know the vowel sound and the first letter, you can use the Index. All the words have two syllables (**).

CLUES	e.g. RHG	ee	– page 167 –	*reaching*
1. LPD		e		_ _ _ _ _ _ _
2. DNF		a		_ _ _ _ _ _ _
3. OCN		oe		_ _ _ _ _
4. GGS		or		_ _ _ _ _ _ _
5. JFY		i		_ _ _ _ _
6. RBY		ue		_ _ _ _
7. RNR		ae		_ _ _ _ _ _ _ _
8. DGN		u		_ _ _ _ _ _

Now complete the puzzle, using the 8 words that you have made.

CLUES

1. an animal with antlers

2. a precious red stone

3. an underground prison

4. lovely

5. a great expanse of water

6. a moment

7. a hair condition

8. a wild animal with spots

TRICKY WORD ENDINGS 1

The vowel spellings are missing in these words, but each word ends with a neutral vowel sound, spelt **ar**, **er** or **or**. You must work out the answers from the clues and check them (especially the endings) in the ACE Dictionary or in the wordsearch below. Write in the missing vowel spellings.

CLUES

1. the person who keeps an eye on prisoners

j _ _ l _ _

2. a machine that sets you in motion

m _ t _ _

3. a tool or handle to start a machine or raise something

l _ v _ _

4. a person who does not tell the truth

l _ _ _

5. someone who gives something (e.g. blood)

d _ n _ _

6. a tall support

p _ ll _ _

Find the above six words in the wordsearch and circle them. Can you find and circle another four words with neutral vowel endings? The words go in the following directions: → ↓ ↘

```
p  e  f  l  a  r  i  q  s  o
d  t  e  f  a  r  m  e  r  t
l  g  p  i  r  s  o  n  a  e
e  d  o  u  v  o  t  e  r  n
s  p  o  d  o  n  o  r  a  j
l  c  i  i  n  u  r  o  z  a
e  a  t  l  b  k  l  e  o  i
v  s  u  n  l  c  a  i  r  l
e  c  k  f  y  a  i  l  a  e
r  l  m  o  w  e  r  s  t  r
```

Now write out six of the words you have found and think of a word which rhymes with each. The rhyming words do not have to end with the same spelling, but the endings must sound the same, e.g. 'peculiar' and 'Julia'. Check the spellings in the ACE Dictionary before you write the words down.

1. _____   rhymes with   _____

2. _____   rhymes with   _____

3. _____   rhymes with   _____

4. _____   rhymes with   _____

5. _____   rhymes with   _____

6. _____   rhymes with   _____

© **LDA** ACE Spelling Activities

TRICKY WORD ENDINGS ❷

The vowel spellings are missing in these words, but each word ends with a neutral vowel sound, spelt **an**, **en**, **in** or **on**. You must work out the answers from the clues and check them (especially the endings) in the ACE Dictionary or in the wordsearch below. Write in the missing vowel spellings.

CLUES

1. to become firm and solid   h _ _ d _ _

2. to become stronger   t _ _ gh _ _

3. a relative   c _ _ s _ _

4. salted pork   b _ c _ _

5. to cover with the darkest colour   bl _ ck _ _

6. claw of a bird of prey   t _ l _ _

Find the above six words in the wordsearch and circle them. Can you find and circle another four words with neutral vowel endings? The words go in the following directions: → ↓ ↘

```
e  b  l  a  c  k  e  n  d  o
s  r  i  p  w  r  s  t  o  s
d  y  s  t  o  r  u  n  s  e
c  e  b  i  m  e  t  r  i  a
w  o  e  h  a  r  d  e  n  s
a  b  u  p  n  s  i  s  i  o
y  a  s  s  e  t  a  l  o  n
o  c  c  a  i  n  t  l  e  d
r  o  t  t  e  n  r  e  f  i
s  n  u  t  o  u  g  h  e  n
```

Now write out six of the words you have found and think of a word which rhymes with each. The rhyming words do not have to end with the same spelling, but the endings must sound the same, e.g. 'peculiar' and 'Julia'. Check the spellings in the ACE Dictionary before you write the words down.

1. _____ rhymes with _____

2. _____ rhymes with _____

3. _____ rhymes with _____

4. _____ rhymes with _____

5. _____ rhymes with _____

6. _____ rhymes with _____

TRICKY WORD ENDINGS ③

The vowel spellings are missing in these words, but each word ends with **cian**, **sion** or **tion**. You must work out the answers from the clues and check them (especially the endings) in the ACE Dictionary or in the wordsearch below. Write in the missing vowel spellings.

CLUES

1. country   n _ _ _ _ n

2. job   _ cc _ p _ _ _ _ n

3. crash   c _ l _ _ _ _ _ n

4. meeting of a court   s _ s _ _ _ n

5. movement   m _ _ _ _ n

6. strong feeling   p _ s _ _ _ n

7. person who does clever tricks   m _ g _ _ _ _ n

8. a shortened word   _ bbr _ v _ _ _ _ _ n

9. answer to a problem   s _ l _ _ _ _ n

10. a person who makes and sells glasses   _ pt _ _ _ _ n

Find and circle in the wordsearch all the 10 words listed above. Can you find and circle another 3 words with **tion** endings? The words go in the following directions: → ↓ ↘

```
m o t i o n l f a v o t
a b b r e v i a t i o n
g p c r e a t s i o c o
i a o p t i f v a p c p
c s l t s a u e l t u s
i s l b i n t x o i p e
a i i w f o r a t c a s
n o s u r e n t i i t s
i n i l t o d i o a i i
o s o l u t i o n n o o
n i n a t i o n t o n n
s e c r e t i n s i d e
```

69

TRICKY WORD ENDINGS ④

The vowel spellings are missing in these words, but each word ends with **ary**, **ery** or **ory**. You must work out the answers from the clues and check them (especially the endings) in the ACE Dictionary or in the wordsearch below. Write in the missing vowel spellings.

1. finding something new   d _ sc _ v _ r _

2. a place where young children are cared for   n _ _ s _ r _

3. good enough   s _ t _ sf _ ct _ r _

4. highly unusual   _ xtr _ _ _ d _ n _ r _

5. getting something back   r _ c _ v _ r _

6. expressing praise   c _ mpl _ m _ nt _ r _

7. great skill   m _ st _ r _

8. a written account of the past   h _ st _ r _

9. raining from time to time   sh _ _ _ r _

10. defeat of an enemy   v _ ct _ r _

Find and circle in the wordsearch all the 10 words listed above. Can you find and circle another 5 words with **ary**, **ery** or **ory** endings? The words go in the following directions: → ↓ ↘

```
w  d  i  s  c  o  v  e  r  y  e  r  y
e  m  b  r  o  i  d  e  r  y  a  h  e
v  n  a  v  m  e  m  o  r  h  g  s  s
e  u  x  i  p  m  i  l  t  i  r  d  t
r  r  n  c  l  a  e  n  v  s  a  i  m
y  s  a  t  i  s  f  a  c  t  o  r  y
s  e  l  o  m  t  e  r  y  o  r  e  s
h  r  o  r  e  e  n  t  s  r  d  c  t
o  y  i  y  n  r  v  o  r  y  i  t  e
w  a  n  n  t  y  t  a  r  y  n  o  r
e  x  t  r  a  o  r  d  i  n  a  r  y
r  u  r  e  r  e  c  o  v  e  r  y  o
y  e  y  a  y  i  n  e  t  r  y  p  t
```

DOUBLES OR SINGLES ①

Can you complete the words below? You are given the first two sounds, including the vowel.

Try both short and long sounds and see if you can think of an answer that fits the meaning. When you complete the words you will need to decide between single and double consonants: **l** or **ll**, **m** or **mm**, **n** or **nn**, **p** or **pp**, **t** or **tt**. Use the ACE Dictionary to check your answers, or to search for the answer if you are stuck.

MEANING	BEGINNING	WRITE
1. way, method of behaviour	ma	_____
2. hot seasoning	pe	_____
3. person in charge of an aeroplane	pi	_____
4. a toy you ride by pushing with one foot	scoo	_____
5. metal object shot from a gun	bu	_____
6. has been put down on paper	wri	_____
7. a tool for hitting nails	ha	_____
8. the front fold of a jacket or blazer	la	_____
9. a yellow spread for bread	bu	_____
10. a carved Red Indian pole	to	_____

Do the double consonants follow a particular type of vowel sound?
Are there any exceptions to the rule?

© **LDA** ACE Spelling Activities

DOUBLES OR SINGLES ❷

Can you complete the words below? You are given the first two sounds, including the vowel.

Try both short and long sounds and see if you can think of an answer that fits the meaning. When you complete the words you will need to decide between single and double consonants: **l** or **ll**, **m** or **mm**, **n** or **nn**, **p** or **pp**, **t** or **tt**. Use the ACE Dictionary to check your answers, or to search for the answer if you are stuck.

MEANING	BEGINNING	WRITE
1. a green salad vegetable	le	_____
2. a person's rank in a group	sta	_____
3. to tease or vex	a	_____
4. lavatory	toi	_____
5. a large passenger boat	li	_____
6. a person who plays the drums	dru	_____
7. excellent	su	_____
8. a citrus fruit	le	_____
9. sickness	il	_____
10. a glowing light round a saint's head	ha	_____

Do the double consonants follow a particular type of vowel sound?
Are there any exceptions to the rule?

FIND THE MIDDLE SYLLABLE

The short (a) sound as in CAT

Sometimes the middle of a long word is the hardest part to spell.

This exercise will help you to spell difficult longer words. Say the words slowly and clearly to yourself and fill in the missing letters.

You can check all your answers by looking in the *** (3-syllable) columns of the ACE Spelling Dictionary.

CLUES		WRITE
e.g. a hard-fired paint	e _ _ _ el	*enamel*
1. device to help you float safely to earth	par _ chute	
2. twisted and caught up	en _ _ _ gled	
3. an unmarried man	bach _ lor	
4. eye make-up	mas _ _ ra	
5. brave, courageous	val _ ant	
6. picture made by sewing on canvas	tap _ _ try	
7. a spear thrown at a sports event	jav _ lin	
8. a large warship	bat _ _ _ ship	
9. taking numbers away	sub _ _ _ _ tion	
10. to make a product well known	ad _ _ _ tise	
11. to desert, to leave	a _ _ _ don	
12. a cloth or tissue for wiping the nose	hand _ _ _ chief	
13. in a furious manner	an _ _ _ ly	
14. living creatures	an _ mals	
15. well-known	fa _ _ _ iar	

73

FIND THE MIDDLE SYLLABLE

The short (e) sound as in ELEPHANT

Sometimes the middle of a long word is the hardest part to spell.

This exercise will help you to spell difficult longer words. Say the words slowly and clearly to yourself and fill in the missing letters.

You can check all your answers by looking in the *** (3-syllable) columns of the ACE Spelling Dictionary.

CLUES		**WRITE**
e.g. recall of events and experiences	mem _ _ y	*memory*
1. one who examines a thing carefully	ins _ _ _ _ or	_____
2. skin colour and appearance	com _ _ _ _ ion	_____
3. framework of bones	skel _ ton	_____
4. rubber boot	wel _ _ _ _ ton	_____
5. severely frighten	ter _ _ fy	_____
6. easily hurt or broken	del _ cate	_____
7. fun and laughter	mer _ _ ment	_____
8. instructions for preparing food	re _ _ pe	_____
9. a punishment	pen _ _ ty	_____
10. deer meat	ven _ son	_____
11. a place to eat	res _ _ _ rant	_____
12. able to bend easily	flex _ ble	_____
13. unpleasant, attack	of _ _ _ sive	_____
14. someone who expects the worst	pes _ _ mist	_____
15. scale of temperature	Cel _ _ us	_____

FIND THE MIDDLE SYLLABLE
The short (i) sound as in PIG

Sometimes the middle of a long word is the hardest part to spell.

This exercise will help you to spell difficult longer words. Say the words slowly and clearly to yourself and fill in the missing letters.

You can check all your answers by looking in the *** (3-syllable) columns of the ACE Spelling Dictionary.

CLUES		WRITE
e.g. person who performs tricks	ma _ _ cian	*magician*
1. high-ranking soldier	brig _ dier	
2. long-legged pink bird	fla _ _ _ go	
3. delicately beautiful	ex _ _ _ site	
4. not taking proper care	ne _ _ _ _ _ ful	
5. dangerous or evil-looking	sin _ _ ter	
6. weakly joined and easily broken	rick _ _ y	
7. small river flowing into a larger one	trib _ tary	
8. an ice-cream flavour	va _ _ _ la	
9. purpose or plan	in _ _ _ tion	
10. hand gun	re _ _ _ ver	
11. go on happening	con _ _ _ ue	
12. a choice or judgement	de _ _ sion	
13. opposite of multiplication	di _ _ sion	
14. talking something over with someone	dis _ _ _ sion	
15. very hard	dif _ _ cult	

FIND THE MIDDLE SYLLABLE

The short (O) sound as in DOG

Sometimes the middle of a long word is the hardest part to spell.

This exercise will help you to spell difficult longer words. Say the words slowly and clearly to yourself and fill in the missing letters.

You can check all your answers by looking in the ∗∗∗ (3-syllable) columns of the ACE Spelling Dictionary.

	CLUES		WRITE
	e.g. eight-sided shape	oc _ _ gon	*octagon*
1.	a chesty illness	bron _ _ _ tis	
2.	a long passage	cor _ _ dor	
3.	being alone	sol _ tude	
4.	a person who offers unpaid help	vol _ _ teer	
5.	an American Indian axe	tom _ hawk	
6.	a building for people who are ill	hos _ _ tal	
7.	making idle talk about other people	gos _ _ _ ing	
8.	a biting insect that spreads malaria	mos _ _ _ to	
9.	greatly surprised	as _ _ _ ished	
10.	deny the statement of another person	con _ _ _ dict	
11.	something put up as a memorial	mon _ ment	
12.	more likely than not	prob _ _ ly	
13.	suitably, correctly	prop _ _ ly	
14.	in a determined way	dog _ _ _ ly	
15.	huge	co _ _ _ sal	

FIND THE MIDDLE SYLLABLE
The short (U) sound as in DUCK

Sometimes the middle of a long word is the hardest part to spell.

This exercise will help you to spell difficult longer words. Say the words slowly and clearly to yourself and fill in the missing letters.

You can check all your answers by looking in the ✱✱✱ (3-syllable) columns of the ACE Spelling Dictionary.

CLUES		**WRITE**
e.g. unwilling to do something	re _ _ _ tant	*reluctant*
1. a large cow-like animal	buf _ _ lo	_____
2. brawny, stronglooking	mus _ _ lar	_____
3. disgusting	re _ _ _ sive	_____
4. marvellous	won _ _ _ ful	_____
5. a large honey-making insect	bum _ _ _ bee	_____
6. a person who buys something	cus _ _ _ er	_____
7. plenty	a _ _ _ dance	_____
8. increase in number	mul _ _ ply	_____
9. lacking awareness through the senses	un _ _ _ scious	_____
10. guessing about what is happening	won _ _ _ ing	_____
11. one-storey house	bun _ _ low	_____
12. one more of the same kind	an _ _ _ er	_____
13. try to stop by showing disapproval	dis _ _ _ rage	_____
14. a dried seedless grape	sul _ _ na	_____
15. quickly and unexpectedly	sud _ _ _ ly	_____

FIND THE MIDDLE SYLLABLE

The long (ae) sound as in SNAIL

Sometimes the middle of a long word is the hardest part to spell.

This exercise will help you to spell difficult longer words. Say the words slowly and clearly to yourself and fill in the missing letters.

You can check all your answers by looking in the *** (3-syllable) columns of the ACE Spelling Dictionary.

CLUES		WRITE
e.g. small peach-like fruit	a _ _ _ cot	*apricot*
1. calmly and without complaining	pa _ _ _ _ _ _ ly	
2. stone parts of a building	ma _ _ _ ry	
3. envelopes and writing material	sta _ _ _ _ ery	
4. great surprise or wonder	a _ _ _ _ ment	
5. storyteller	nar _ _ tor	
6. fixing a name to	la _ _ _ ling	
7. in error	mis _ _ ken	
8. local area	neigh _ _ _ _ hood	
9. likely to cause harm	dan _ _ _ ous	
10. large serving spoon	ta _ _ _ spoon	
11. in a trembling manner	sha _ _ ly	
12. unable to wait	im _ _ tient	
13. a holiday period	va _ _ tion	
14. annoyed disappointment	frus _ _ _ tion	
15. large sports area for spectators	sta _ _ um	

FIND THE MIDDLE SYLLABLE

The long (ee) sound as in EAGLE

Sometimes the middle of a long word is the hardest part to spell.

This exercise will help you to spell difficult longer words. Say the words slowly and clearly to yourself and fill in the missing letters.

You can check all your answers by looking in the *** (3-syllable) columns of the ACE Spelling Dictionary.

CLUES		WRITE
e.g. programme written in parts	se _ _ al	*serial*
1. came before	pre _ _ ded	
2. successful outcome	a _ _ _ _ _ _ ment	
3. strong and passionate	ve _ _ ment	
4. tiredness	wea _ _ ness	
5. a means of land transport	ve _ _ cle	
6. boring and tiring	te _ _ ous	
7. coming earlier in time or order	pre _ _ ous	
8. food in the form of grain	ce _ _ al	
9. restore confidence	re _ _ sure	
10. even-handedly, to the same degree	eq _ _ _ _ y	
11. too proud, puffed up	con _ _ _ _ ed	
12. attractive countryside	sce _ _ ry	
13. gentle, merciful	le _ _ ent	
14. with genuine feeling	sin _ _ _ _ ly	
15. newspapers, television and radio	me _ _ a	

FIND THE MIDDLE SYLLABLE
The long (ie) sound as in LION

Sometimes the middle of a long word is the hardest part to spell.

This exercise will help you to spell difficult longer words. Say the words slowly and clearly to yourself and fill in the missing letters.

You can check all your answers by looking in the *** (3-syllable) columns of the ACE Spelling Dictionary.

CLUES		**WRITE**
e.g. a very hard precious stone	di _ mond	*diamond*
1. causing lively feelings	ex _ _ _ ing	
2. moving home each season	mi _ _ _ ting	
3. a three-sided shape	tri _ _ gle	
4. a musical instrument with flat bars	xy _ _ phone	
5. a collection of books	li _ _ _ ry	
6. task	as _ _ _ _ ment	
7. unbelievably huge	gi _ _ _ tic	
8. the line where sky and earth meet	ho _ _ zon	
9. way of earning a living	live _ _ hood	
10. joyfully successful	tri _ _ phant	
11. the material of elephant tusks	i _ _ ry	
12. offering something to influence judgement	br _ _ ery	
13. to do with money	fi _ _ _ cial	
14. a person who prepares a plan	de _ _ _ _ er	
15. one who remains alive after danger	sur _ _ vor	

FIND THE MIDDLE SYLLABLE

The long (oe) sound as in GOAT

Sometimes the middle of a long word is the hardest part to spell.

This exercise will help you to spell difficult longer words. Say the words slowly and clearly to yourself and fill in the missing letters.

You can check all your answers by looking in the *** (3-syllable) columns of the ACE Spelling Dictionary.

CLUES		**WRITE**
e.g. left out	o _ _ _ ted	*omitted*
1. a strong (usually pleasant) smell	a _ _ ma	
2. unable to move	im _ _ bile	
3. lawful possession	ow _ _ _ ship	
4. steady affection, strong commitment	de _ _ tion	
5. food and household supplies	gro _ _ ries	
6. leaves	fo _ _ age	
7. very bad, shocking	a _ _ _ cious	
8. friendly, liking company	so _ _ _ ble	
9. lacking and wanting human contact	lone _ _ ness	
10. a strong feeling	e _ _ tion	
11. hateful, repulsive, very unpleasant	o _ _ ous	
12. a large fibre-covered nut	co _ _ nut	
13. fierce	fe _ _ cious	
14. cheerily good-natured, jolly	jo _ _ al	
15. an orchestral stringed instrument	vi _ la	

© **LDA** ACE Spelling Activities

FIND THE MIDDLE SYLLABLE

The long (OO) sound as in SMOOTH and (ue) as in NEWT

Sometimes the middle of a long word is the hardest part to spell.

This exercise will help you to spell difficult longer words. Say the words slowly and clearly to yourself and fill in the missing letters.

You can check all your answers by looking in the *** (3-syllable) columns of the ACE Spelling Dictionary.

CLUES		**WRITE**
e.g. eager to find out, unusual	cu _ _ ous	*curious*
1. where old things may be displayed	mu _ _ um	_____
2. stamina, the ability to survive	en _ _ _ ance	_____
3. an exact copy	du _ _ _ cate	_____
4. shaped like a hollow pipe	tu _ _ lar	_____
5. pleasant pastime	a _ _ _ _ ment	_____
6. a time of celebration to mark an event	ju _ _ lee	_____
7. a person who goes by car or train to work	com _ _ ter	_____
8. apply oil	lu _ _ _ cate	_____
9. causing destruction, decayed	ru _ _ ous	_____
10. containing or worked by air	pneu _ _ tic	_____
11. lovely	beau _ _ ful	_____
12. someone who enters without permission	in _ _ _ der	_____
13. very quiet and private	se _ _ _ ded	_____
14. a person escaping from capture	fu _ _ tive	_____
15. shining in the dark	lu _ _ nous	_____

FIND THE MIDDLE SYLLABLE

using all sections of the Dictionary

Sometimes the middle of a long word is the hardest part to spell.

This exercise will help you to spell difficult longer words. Say the words slowly and clearly to yourself and fill in the missing letters.

You can check all your answers by looking in the *** (3-syllable) columns of the ACE Spelling Dictionary.

CLUES		ANIMAL PICTURE CLUE	WRITE
e.g. a food not unlike butter	mar _ _ rine		*margarine*
1. a pair of glasses	spec _ _ cles		
2. tired out, completely used up	ex _ _ _ _ ted		
3. full of energy	vig _ _ ous		
4. a person who designs buildings	ar _ _ _ tect		
5. a clear, fizzy drink	lem _ _ ade		
6. a two-wheeled machine	bi _ _ cle		
7. wonderful	mar _ _ _ lous		
8. a large ape	go _ _ _ la		
9. breaking in and stealing	bur _ _ _ _ y		
10. a person from another country	fo _ _ _ _ _ er		
11. musicians under a conductor	or _ _ _ _ _ ra		
12. a picture made with small tiles	mo _ _ ic		
13. definitely	cer _ _ _ _ ly		
14. full of very high hills	moun _ _ _ _ ous		
15. an arrangement to meet	ap _ _ _ _ _ ment		

FIND THE TWO MIDDLE SYLLABLES

using all sections of the Dictionary ❶

Sometimes the middle of a long word is the hardest part to spell.

This exercise will help you to spell difficult longer words. Say the words slowly and clearly to yourself and fill in the missing letters.

You can check all your answers by looking in the **** (4-syllable) columns of the ACE Spelling Dictionary.

CLUES		ANIMAL PICTURE CLUE	WRITE
e.g. not natural, man-made	ar _ _ _ _ cial		*artificial*
1. triumphant in battle	vic _ _ _ _ _ ous		_____
2. not achievable; unbearable	im _ _ _ _ _ _ ble		_____
3. the total number of inhabitants	pop _ _ _ tion		_____
4. surroundings	en _ _ _ _ _ _ ment		_____
5. process of growing or changing	de _ _ _ _ _ _ ment		_____
6. a belief based on ignorant fear	su _ _ _ _ _ _ _ tion		_____
7. capturing images on film	pho _ _ _ _ _ phy		_____
8. exactly the same	i _ _ _ _ _ _ cal		_____
9. absurd	ri _ _ _ _ lous		_____
10. looking or sounding good	fa _ _ _ _ _ ble		_____
11. a measurement of distance	kil _ _ _ tre		_____
12. the smallest part of a group	mi _ _ _ _ ty		_____
13. making a person feel awkward	em _ _ _ _ _ _ _ ing		_____
14. something put up in remembrance	me _ _ _ _ al		_____
15. unplanned, done on impulse	spon _ _ _ _ ous		_____

FIND THE TWO MIDDLE SYLLABLES

using all sections of the Dictionary ❷

Sometimes the middle of a long word is the hardest part to spell.

This exercise will help you to spell difficult longer words. Say the words slowly and clearly to yourself and fill in the missing letters.

You can check all your answers by looking in the **** (4-syllable) columns

CLUES		ANIMAL PICTURE CLUE	WRITE
e.g. clever	in _ _ _ _ _ gent		*intelligent*
1. well-known for something bad	no _ _ _ _ ous		
2. a ceremony of crowning	co _ _ _ _ tion		
3. to build up or collect	ac _ _ _ _ late		
4. not lasting	tem _ _ _ _ ry		
5. owner of a business or building	pro _ _ _ _ tor		
6. savings in outgoing costs	e _ _ _ _ mies		
7. make known	com _ _ _ _ cate		
8. plant growth	veg _ _ _ tion		
9. causing much laughter	hi _ _ _ _ ous		
10. study of the heavenly bodies	as _ _ _ _ _ my		
11. large self-service store	su _ _ _ _ _ _ ket		
12. meat-eating	car _ _ _ _ rous		
13. a severe throat infection	ton _ _ _ _ tis		
14. strange, special	pe _ _ _ _ ar		
15. at right angles to vertical	hor _ _ _ _ tal		

WORDS WITHIN WORDS ①

Find the baseword or simplest form of each word and write it in the box. To do this remove the word ending. Take care with double consonants and with basewords which end with a 'magic e'.

Then, using the ACE Dictionary, find another word which starts with the baseword and write it on the line. The longer word must have at least 3 more letters than the baseword.

CLUES	BASEWORD	WRITE
e.g. sunny	sun	*sunburnt*
1. safety		
2. careless		
3. fitted		
4. funniest		
5. rocky		
6. thundered		
7. netting		
8. raindrop		
9. downstairs		
10. earthed		
11. shopper		
12. slipped		
13. footstep		
14. brightly		
15. sometimes		

WORDS WITHIN WORDS ❷

Find the baseword or simplest form of each word and write it in the box. To do this remove the word ending. Take care with double consonants and with basewords which end with a 'magic e'.

Then, using the ACE Dictionary, find another word which starts with the baseword and write it on the line. The longer word must have at least 3 more letters than the baseword.

CLUES	BASEWORD	WRITE
e.g. thirsty	thirst	*thirstiness*
1. circled		
2. dirty		
3. cheerfully		
4. imagined		
5. wholly		
6. dreaded		
7. infectious		
8. memorise		
9. chaotic		
10. governor		
11. merciful		
12. greedy		
13. scientist		
14. mountaineer		
15. agreeable		

FIND THE BASEWORD OR ROOT ①

Basewords are simple words with basic meaning of words derived from them. You can often find them on the same page of the ACE Dictionary as the words based on them.

Underline the correct meaning of each numbered word. Write the root or baseword in the box.

| CLUES | e.g. the baseword for **personality** is **person** |
| | e.g. the baseword for **leadership** is **lead** |

1. politely
   a) in a well-mannered way
   b) in a clever way

2. explosion
   a) unprotected from the weather
   b) a loud noise when something is blown up

3. miner
   a) less important
   b) a mineworker

4. plantation
   a) a large group of trees grown by people
   b) a garden centre

5. serial
   a) a breakfast dish
   b) parts of a story in order

6. scornfully
   a) walking painfully on sore feet
   b) mockingly

7. globally
   a) circular in shape
   b) worldwide

8. reliable
   a) able to relay a message
   b) dependable

9. simplicity
   a) an uncomplicated state
   b) stupidity

10. fictitious
    a) fierce
    b) invented, untrue

FIND THE BASEWORD OR ROOT ②

Basewords are simple words with basic meaning of words derived from them. You can often find them on the same page of the ACE Dictionary as the words based on them.

Underline the correct meaning of each numbered word. Write the root or baseword in the box.

| **CLUES** | e.g. the baseword for **numerous** is **number**
e.g. the baseword for **migration** is **migrate** |

1. mortally
   a) made with bricks and mortar
   b) fatally

2. liberation
   a) the experience of being set free
   b) a group of librarians

3. joyfully
   a) showing pleasure and excitement
   b) joining two things

4. optician
   a) one who looks on the bright side
   b) one who tests eyesight

5. navigator
   a) an explorer
   b) one who chooses the correct direction

6. review
   a) a survey or critical account
   b) a theatrical entertainment

7. streamer
   a) a little stream
   b) a paper decoration

8. employee
   a) someone who offers work
   b) someone who gets paid for work

9. lessen
   a) reduce
   b) a period of instruction

10. accepted
    a) not included
    b) received

INTRODUCING THE PARTS OF SPEECH
NOUNS ❶

Words which can have **a** or **the** in front of them are used to name things. They are nouns. In this exercise all the words which fill the gaps are nouns. To help you find them the ACE Dictionary page is given, together with the number of syllables.

PAGE 138

**   1.   The fire _____ was called out after the explosion.

*   2.   At last the fierce _____ was extinguished.

*   3.   Each pony has a _____ of hay in its stable.

**   4.   He gave his wife a silver necklace and _____.

PAGE 200

**   1.   The air _____ demonstrated the safety drill.

**   2.   We stayed in a _____ near the beach.

*   3.   Grandma did not want to live in a retirement _____ .

**   4.   We use a _____ to wash the car.

PAGE 120

*   1.   My little brother likes to bang his toy _____.

**   2.   The baby cries if she loses her _____.

***   3.   It doesn't matter if I get dirt on my _____.

*   4.   The white _____ cooed on the window-sill.

PAGE 246

***   1.   Dad bought new _____ for my bedroom.

*   2.   I gave Mum a pretty green _____ in a pot.

**   3.   Metals are heated in a _____ .

****   4.   Horse manure is an organic _____.

INTRODUCING THE PARTS OF SPEECH

NOUNS ❷

Words which can have **a** or **the** in front of them are used to name things. They are nouns. In this exercise all the words which fill the gaps are nouns. To help you find them the ACE Dictionary page is given, together with the number of syllables.

PAGE 164

*   1.   Mum brought some _____ for Sunday lunch.

**   2.   The weighing _____ did not speak the truth.

**   3.   The doctor said my spots were the _____ .

*   4.   We went to the restaurant for a _____ .

PAGE 240

*   1.   The bus went round the _____.

**   2.   I stuffed an old suit to make a _____ .

*   3.   My brother made me do my _____ of the washing-up.

**   4.   We carried the bed up the _____ .

PAGE 212

***   1.   The boy carried the _____ into the church.

***   2.   I bought some new games for my _____ .

***   3.   We had ham and _____ sandwiches.

*   4.   The detective looked for a _____ to the murder.

PAGE 277

*   1.   There was not a _____ in the sky.

***   2.   The town _____ made a long speech.

*   3.   The Queen wears a _____ when she opens Parliament.

*   4.   I lay on the _____ to watch my favourite TV programme.

INTRODUCING THE PARTS OF SPEECH
VERBS **1**

A verb often follows a noun (or a pronoun such as **we**) to express an action (actual or possible), thought or feeling. In this exercise all the words which fill the gaps are verbs. To help you find them the ACE Dictionary page is given, together with the number of syllables.

PAGE 142

**   1.   We _____ the cake with chocolate.

*   2.   I think that photograph should be enlarged and _____ .

**   3.   I knew the TV was broken when the picture _____ away.

**   4.   Dad _____ us for borrowing his camera without permission.

PAGE 46

*   1.   The hen began to _____ at the food.

**   2.   I hugged and _____ my faithful dog.

***   3.   She was on her bike, _____ very fast.

*   4.   We _____ on, trying to make up lost time.

PAGE 277

**   1.   I was _____ my sweets when the baby grabbed one.

**   2.   The injured man _____ as the soldier raised his rifle.

*   3.   It is time to _____ the carnival queen.

**   4.   We all _____ into the lift instead of using the stairs.

PAGE 133

**   1.   It was hard going, _____ up the steep hill.

*   2.   Kim _____ her tail when I opened a tin of her favourite food.

***   3.   The moles in the garden are always _____ away.

*   4.   Don't _____ that cake until teatime!

INTRODUCING THE PARTS OF SPEECH

VERBS ❷

A verb often follows a noun (or a pronoun such as **we**) to express an action (actual or possible), thought or feeling. In this exercise all the words which fill the gaps are verbs. To help you find them the ACE Dictionary page is given, together with the number of syllables.

PAGE 252

**	1.	I was _____ all over the town for some new trainers.
*	2.	I _____ the pancake mixture thoroughly.
**	3.	The _____ sea heaved the small boat against the rocks.
*	4.	My teacher says I must not _____ doing my homework.

PAGE 192

*	1.	I shall _____ the parcel and take it to the post office.
***	2.	The teacher _____ French lessons for Friday mornings.
*	3.	She_____ to phone her mum, but the phone was out of order.
*	4.	I shall _____the race with my stopwatch.

PAGE 154

**	1.	The invading army _____ the town.
*	2.	She will buy a stud farm and _____ racehorses.
*	3.	We could hardly _____ in the crowded room.
*	4.	We hoped that we would _____ the record.

PAGE 96

**	1.	We spent all morning _____ wood.
*	2.	Make sure there's no traffic before you_____ the road!
***	3.	I had to _____ hard to understand the instructions.
***	4.	Please don't _____ my plans by trying to change them.

INTRODUCING THE PARTS OF SPEECH
ADJECTIVES

Adjectives are words which add to the meaning of names of persons, places, ideas or things. They often answer a question such as 'What is it like?' In this exercise all the words which fill the gaps are adjectives. To help you find them the ACE Dictionary page is given, together with the number of syllables.

PAGE 188

**   1.   She rudely turned down my _____ request.

**   2.   I would love my own _____ helicopter.

**   3.   Do hypnotists really have _____ powers?

***   4.   Five-year-olds go to _____ school.

PAGE 24

***   1.   That big lion looks _____ .

***   2.   The _____ shed was blown down in the gale.

**   3.   The orphan's clothes were torn and _____ .

**   4.   _____ numbers are called out in a bingo session.

PAGE 113

**   1.   Some chemical waste is highly _____ .

***   2.   The _____ rainforests are being destroyed.

**   3.   Ben won a _____ apple at the fair.

**   4.   I have got a _____ headache.

PAGE 263

**   1.   Brian always got smacked when he was _____ .

**   2.   A temperature of 98.4° Fahrenheit is completely _____ .

***   3.   Sailors used to rely on _____ charts.

**   4.   The Tyne is a river in _____ England.

INTRODUCING THE PARTS OF SPEECH
ADVERBS

Adverbs are words which add to the meaning of verbs or adjectives. Many of them end in **–ly**. They answer questions such as 'How?', 'How much?', 'Where?', 'When?' In this exercise all the words which fill the gaps are adverbs. To help you find them the ACE Dictionary page is given, together with the number of syllables.

PAGE 134

*****   1.   _____ , Jim fell through the thin ice.

******   2.   Julie always dressed _____ .

****   3.   Bouncer was _____ the best dog in the show.

***   4.   The ground was rough and stony _____ .

PAGE 190

**   1.   Sharon came forward _____ to receive her prize.

******   2.   The experimental results must be analysed _____ .

***   3.   The small boy nodded _____ .

**   4.   I feel _____ better today.

PAGE 52

*****   1.   The traffic lights were _____ out of action.

****   2.   The violin solo was _____ very difficult.

****   3.   It rained _____ for three hours.

***   4.   After the party we were _____ late to bed.

PAGE 28

***   1.   I replied very _____ , so as not to give offence.

****   2.   They died _____ in a car crash.

*****   3.   The dictator ruled _____ for 25 years.

***   4.   _____ the opposition leader escaped arrest.

SEARCHING FOR PATTERNS

Here are some further ideas for your students, to help them recognize some of the many spelling patterns and the exceptions!

1 When you add **-ing** to words ending with 'e', you knock off the 'e'. This does not apply if the ending is a double vowel (**ee**, **ie**, **ue**). See how many words you can find in 2 minutes that fit this pattern.

2 See how many 3-syllable words you can find where a final 'y' changes to an 'ie'. Group these under the headings: **ies**, **ied** and **ier/iest**.

3 With words like **wit** (with a one-letter vowel and a single final consonant) you double the final consonant when you add endings such as **-ed**, **-ing**, **-er**, **-est**, **-y**, **-ier** and **-iest**. So you get: slow-**witted**, out**witting**, **witty**, **wittier**, **wittiest**. See how many one-syllable words you can find in 2 minutes that fit this pattern.
Are there any exceptions?

4 Find 10 words like **itch** (one syllable, with a single-letter short vowel and the (**tch**) sound right after the vowel).
Find 10 more one-syllable words with a letter between the short vowel and the (**ch**) sound, such as: **belch**, **inch**, **lunch**.
Find 20 words ending in (**ch**) from any of the long vowel sections.
What pattern do you notice? Are there any exceptions?
Can you explain in a simple way when to use **tch**?

Carry out similar searches in order to establish when to use **edge** rather than **ge** and when to use **ck** rather than **k**.

5 'I' before 'e' except after 'c'. What is the ratio of hits to misses if this rule is applied to words in the long vowel (**ee**) section?

6 How many words of four or more syllables in which the last syllable contains a neutral vowel sound can you find in 2 minutes?

7 Make a list of homonym pairs from the (**or**) section where spelling confusion is likely.

8
truthful – truthfully
helpful – helpfully
grateful – gratefully

Full of ......? Find five more words listed in the ACE Dictionary that fit this pattern.

WORDS YOU NEED TO KNOW

Some of the words you meet every day are not easy to write. 'Friend' is one of these unfriendly words. Words which break the law should be treated with suspicion. You need to use an IDENTIKIT card to check the special features of these suspect words. The master list of suspects is on page 98.

WHAT TO DO

1 Put a tick next to each word on the list which you know very well. These words are innocent and may even be friendly. The others will make up your list of suspects. You will find that some of the suspects have split personalities and may seem to be two separate words, although they are really only one.

2 Get a piece of card which will fit into your ACE Dictionary or into your jotter if folded down the middle.

3 Copy your list of suspects, with further particulars if provided, in two columns. You can add some words of your own if you want to. Then use a highlighter pen to mark any special features of the suspect words which will help you to remember them.

4 Make a second copy of your list of suspects on the back of your card, but this time do not add the further particulars. Leave a space or draw a box beside each word so that you can put tally marks to show how many times you have recognized a suspect.

5 Ask a friendly word-inspector to check your IDENTIKIT card when it is ready for use.

6 Get to know your suspects better. Take four words at a time and make up some sentences using these words. Write out your sentences and when you get to a suspect word, find it on your card so you can copy it. Try to copy it after looking at it once only and as you write it notice any special features. When you have finished, ask your friendly word-inspector to double-check what you have written, using your card and the ACE Dictionary if necessary.

HOW TO USE YOUR IDENTIKIT CARD

Get your card out every time you do some writing. Whenever a suspect word comes along, check it out on your card before you write it down. Every time you do this, turn your card over and put a tally mark next to the word. You can cross off suspect words when you no longer need to check them on your card, but you should not do this until you have at least ten tally marks against a word.

© LDA ACE Spelling Activities

IDENTIKIT MASTER LIST OF SUSPECT WORDS

again	
always	(al/ _ _ _ _)
an	(a . . e . . i . . o . . u . .)
another	
bought	
caught	(did catch)
decided	
friend	
heard	(_ ear _)
hour	(60 minutes)
inside	
into	
it's	(it is)
kept	
knew	(silent k)
know	(silent k)
lot	(a lot)
might	(?igh?)
myself	
off	(not on)
opened	
outside	
police	

right	(✓ or →)
running	
sometimes	
still	
stopped	
suddenly	
their	(ownership)
there	(there is . . . there are . . . there was . . . there were . . . there will be . . . there would be . . . there could be . . . etc. → to or in that place)
thought	
through	(by way of)
too	(too much/as well)
tried	
turned	
until	(_ _ til/)
want	
were	(in the past)
where	(place)

It is a good idea to make a new IDENTIKIT card once a term until you have narrowed down your list of suspects to one or two dangerous individuals. If you succeed in doing this you will have reduced the crime rate by up to 20%.

HOW TO REMEMBER THE SPECIAL FEATURES OF THE
MOST DANGEROUS SUSPECTS

always	This is **always** one word with one **l**, all the time.
an	An egg, **an** anything beginning with **a e i o u**.
caught.....	Her naughty daughter **caught** a cold.
heard.......	Did hear, by **ear**.
hour	60 minutes.
it's	**It's** short for 'it is' and the ' stands for the letter **i**.
knew........	(silent **k**) – understood.
know........	(silent **k**) – understand?
lot	'**A lot**' is NOT one word.
might	I **might** get it right!
off	On and off, '**off**' is confused with '**of**'.
right	Did you write it on the **right** and get it **right**?
their	Our dog is ours, not yours – **their** dog is theirs.
there	Here and **there there** are some rare bears.
through....	Although it was rough, he thought we would get **through**.
too	Not TOO many **o**'s to count in twos!
until.........	One 'l' as in **1–nil**: unlike fill, hill, kill, pill, till, will.
were	Why **were** we waiting when the light was green?
where	**Where** were you when the fire broke out in that place?

© **LDA** ACE Spelling Activities

LEARN TO SPELL THESE REALLY USEFUL WORDS

and get them right when you write!

Three lists of 220 useful words have been prepared from samples of children's speech and writing. The lists do not include the 40 common words which are most often misspelt. Those words are best learned by using the IDENTIKIT card in the course of writing. Simple words which present no spelling problems have been left out. Taken together, the three lists plus the 40 IDENTIKIT words account for between 40% and 60% of the words found in children's writing at ages 9–11.

Each list can be covered in one term, at the rate of 20 words a week. This allows for some repeated learning of words misspelt in weekly tests. Lists 1, 2 and 3 are suitable for N.C. Levels 2, 3 and 4–5 respectively and for Scottish levels A, B and C.

Students who need an accelerated spelling programme can work on the lists for a whole year.

USING THE THREE LISTS

It is not intended that the same list should be given to all members of a class. All three lists are needed in order to provide for a typical range of ability and teachers may want to add others which are more or less demanding. The following tests can be used to decide which list should be used by which students.

SPELLING TEST

Say each word, repeat it in a phrase or sentence, pause briefly and then say the word again.

1. SHIP . . . The passengers boarded the SHIP . . . . SHIP

2. FOOTBALL . . . My FOOTBALL strip . . . . FOOTBALL

3. READING . . . What are you READING? . . . . READING

4. TELL . . . TELL me a story . . . . TELL

5. SEVEN . . . SEVEN puppies in a basket . . . . SEVEN

6. SPOKE . . . I SPOKE to Gran on the phone . . . . SPOKE

7. SLOWLY . . . We walked very SLOWLY . . . . SLOWLY

8. NEAR . . . We live NEAR the park . . . . NEAR

9. PERSON . . . Who is that PERSON crossing the road? . . . . PERSON

10. ANYTHING . . . Have you ANYTHING to report? . . . . ANYTHING

11. PRETTY . . . The garden was looking very PRETTY . . . . PRETTY

12. BEFORE . . . Tidy your room BEFORE you go out . . . . BEFORE

13. OWNER . . . Who is the OWNER of this car? . . . . OWNER

14. MUSIC . . . I listen to MUSIC on my Walkman . . . . MUSIC

15. HAPPENED . . . What HAPPENED in the playground? . . . . HAPPENED

16. FOLLOWED . . . The stray dog FOLLOWED me . . . . FOLLOWED

17. SUGAR . . . SUGAR in your tea . . . . SUGAR

18. MOUNTAIN . . . The top of the MOUNTAIN . . . . MOUNTAIN

19. USUAL . . . I woke up at seven, as USUAL . . . . USUAL

20. INTERESTING . . . An INTERESTING story . . . . INTERESTING

Students scoring   0–4   should work with List 1
5–14 should work with List 2
15–20 should work with List 3

The 220 words in each list have been grouped into sets of four words, on the basis of a topic or language pattern. There are five word sets across the page; five sets are enough for a week's work. Nouns, verbs, adjectives and adverbs have been grouped together, with some miscellaneous sets at the end. This makes it easier to think of meaningful links between words and to use the words in sentences.

Note that words with an asterisk (∗) against them may need special attention, as it is hard or impossible to find a rhyming word with the same spelling pattern. You may be able to think of a non-rhyming word with the same letter string (e.g. watch/match) or find some other way of remembering the letters.

The word sets are not arranged in order of difficulty.

INDIVIDUAL LISTS

Students can follow individual paths, so that they do not study words they can already spell. The alphabetical lists can be used in this way.

Every fortnight students choose 20, 40 or 60 words to learn from one of the lists. These are words which the student would like to be able to spell. The words are underlined and then written down in sets of four. If possible, there should be some meaningful link between the words in a set, as this makes the words and their spellings easier to remember. Students can choose words that will fit into a sentence, that are linked by topic or that have the same spelling pattern. If the lists are exhausted, words may be taken from other sources.

With individual lists, individual daily tests are needed. This is best organized in pairs with students testing each other.

Another kind of individual list, for use in correcting drafts (N.C. Level 3, Scottish level C, and above) is described on pages 104–105.

HOW TO LEARN

If you look at words in a list and have someone test you, you may not remember the spellings very well. A more active approach will lead to better results. You should STUDY – COPY – CHECK – HIGHLIGHT and then LEARN. Try the different methods of learning given below and decide which work best for you.

STUDY	– look at the word and count the syllables
COPY	– you are allowed only one glance per syllable
CHECK	– letter by letter or in strings of up to four letters
HIGHLIGHT	– mark the parts you need to remember
LEARN	– by one or more of these methods:

(a) pronounce the words in a different way, according to the spelling

(b) trace over or write the word, saying the letter names before you write each letter string

(c) shut your eyes and say or spell the word as you 'write' it in large letters with your finger

(d) with eyes shut see the word in your mind, count the letters in groups and then check

(e) study the word, say a tongue-twister or count to 10, then spell the word

(f) think of a memory link or mnemonic for the whole word or just for the tricky part (e.g. On **Fri**day and at the week**end** I'll see my friends. **F**ind **R**eally **I**nteresting **FRI**ends.)

(g) use the ACE Dictionary to find a word which rhymes with the one you are learning and is spelt in the same way; think of a rhyme and then check the spelling, or simply look through the 1- and 2-syllable columns in a single vowel section

Note: words marked * do not have suitable rhymes.

(h) find another word you already know which has the same spelling pattern (e.g. tongue, argue)

(i) learn the tricky part (or parts) first, before trying the whole word

REPEAT – say, write and spell really rapidly, like a R–A–PP–E–R

TEST – look, cover, write, check

At the end of a learning session, write down a sentence containing the words you have studied. This may help you to spell those words correctly later on when you are writing – which is the whole point!

THE DAILY ROUTINE

Every day you will study two, four or six words from your list. It is helpful if the words are related in some way. Enter the date and the words to be learned in a jotter.

Steps to success

1st word	– learn (using chosen method)
self-test	– look – cover – write – check
2nd word	– learn
self-test	– look – cover – write – check
double-check	– look at both words – cover – write – check Continue if both words are correct: otherwise practise and try the test again.
3rd word	– learn
self-test	– look – cover – write – check
4th word	– learn
self-test	– look – cover – write – check
double-check	– look at both words – cover – write – check Continue if both words are correct: otherwise practise and try the test again.
final test	– all four words should be written correctly when dictated in a random order

 © **LDA** ACE Spelling Activities

If you do not pass the final test, you must try to learn the words again, perhaps by a different method. On the other hand it may be better to attempt two words instead of four.

When you succeed on the final test, a responsible person should initial the list in your jotter and record the learning method(s) from (a) to (i).

If you find four words easy to learn, you might like to work with groups of six instead.

Note that if you are trying to learn six words you can double-check with groups of two or three words.

THE WEEKLY TEST

Once a week, test sessions should be set up in pairs, so that each learner both gives and receives a test on the 8, 16 or 24 words chosen for that week. Words spelt correctly should be given a tick in the jotter and on the master list. Those not spelt correctly may be studied again the following week, but if so they should be spaced out over the week.

SPELLING CORRECTLY AND CORRECTING MISTAKES

If you use the **STUDY – COPY – CHECK – HIGHLIGHT – LEARN** approach, you will probably make fewer mistakes with words you have recently studied. You can hardly expect that you will never again have to think about those words. Indeed, every time you realize that you have used a word that is on your list or seems to fit a familiar pattern, you score a success. All you then have to do is to check the spelling. If it is correct, that is EXCELLENT!

Good spellers are aware of common patterns between 'families' of words. The more often you look up words in the ACE Spelling Dictionary, the more you will notice these patterns. Looking for word families based on Lists 1–3 can introduce you to thousands of words. Learning method (g) (looking up rhyming words) is one of the best ways of 'getting to know' more word families. This method also encourages you to use a wider vocabulary when you write.

Most people miss spelling mistakes when they read through a piece of work. You can improve at this if you make a personal alphabetical list of the words you want to learn from Lists 1, 2 and 3. It is sensible to include some interesting words from the same 'families' and any hard-to-spell words you have previously attempted. If you arrange the list in syllable columns, as in the ACE Spelling Dictionary, it will be easier to scan. Read through the list before you check your draft: this will make it much more likely that you will recognise the words in the piece you have written.

Your list might look like this:

*	* *	* * * (+)
aren't	against	ambulance
board	allow	arrival
break	answer	beautiful
brought	answered	disappeared
clothes	believe	February
course	buried	hospital
guard	curtain	idea
it's	harbour	investigate
knocked	haunted	parliament
let's	later	remembered
passed	people	suitable
past	present	unfortunately
piece	quickly	vegetables
race	really	
spare	swimming	
they're	themselves	
threw	without	
you're		

It is a good idea to check your draft at least three times, each time concentrating on a limited range of words. First, look for any words of three or more syllables which need to be checked. Then go through the passage again, looking for two-syllable words which might present problems. Finally, concentrate on one-syllable words, taking care not to skim over words such as 'its', 'they' and 'was' which do not 'leap off the page'.

The more often you correct your own spelling mistakes, the better your spelling will become. When you know how to put things right, you can really concentrate on what you are writing.

© LDA ACE Spelling Activities

LIST 1

Number of Words in the Word List: 220

father	baby	dog	bus	money
dad	babies	hair	car	gold
mother	boy	way	road	bank
mum	girl	park	street	shop
look	ask	come	be	* are
looked	asked	* coming	been	will
find	call	came	* being	could
found	called	went	stay	couldn't
one	some	bad	* front	* his
* two	left	good	ready	* her
three	all	better	nice	our
four	more	best	happy	your
garden	door	tea	book	king
farm	room	water	story	queen
wood	window	time	bed	lady
sea	fire	things	night	man
go	* was	woke	see	catch
goes	* wasn't	help	saw	make
going	would	told	* put	made
gone	wouldn't	sleep	seen	eat
black	big	next	my	away
blue	little	last	* this	around
red	new	long	that	back
white	old	round	other	home
* children	* morning	* Christmas	* woman	* people
sister	* afternoon	tree	teacher	name
brother	week	day	school	hand
* aunt	year	dinner	work	* eyes
do	* has	give	dance	* watch
don't	* have	gave	walk	* watching
did	* having	take	walking	start
didn't	had	took	walked	started
when	how	first	no	by
just	so	* once	yes	for
now	down	out	* very	with
then	here	over	well	without
giant	he	him	* who	please
* castle	she	himself	* someone	me
ghost	we	you	which	* that's
house	they	them	* something	much
play	named	like	upon	or
playing	think	married	about	but
played	say	live	* from	* because
fell	* said	* lived	after	while

LIST ②

Number of Words in the Word List: 220

* aeroplane	* animals	present	* clothes	prince
air	bird	balloon	* body	princess
plane	snake	* colour	* shoes	life
* world	* horse	* music	foot	love
tell	listen	read	point	hold
spoke	listened	reading	write	* build
shouted	* answer	mean	writing	built
hear	* answered	meant	written	* covered
* these	high	* every	wide	* usual
those	* higher	its	* straight	* different
any	smaller	sure	near	* interesting
many	short	true	real	* coloured
wife	* family	* sugar	boat	* football
* husband	table	* breakfast	ship	field
* person	chair	meat	shape	line
* group	* kitchen	* course	* owner	* corner
hope	pick	drop	try	* finish
hoped	picked	dropped	trying	* finished
hoping	pull	break	cry	leave
getting	* pulled	* breaking	cried	fly
* young	whole	tired	dead	* nearby
* beautiful	closed	* lonely	broken	* maybe
* pretty	past	dark	dry	quite
dear	seven	* careful	strange	alright
* machine	dragon	ears	* word	* radio
wheel	head	nose	* idea	station
hole	* heart	mouth	* notice	* minutes
light	blood	* voice	* language	* sentence
seemed	die	sitting	meet	should
* imagine	died	waiting	brought	* does
guess	jumped	* happen	passed	* doesn't
* understand	killed	* happened	followed	done
quickly	already	* even	nearly	onto
slowly	behind	* also	* usually	across
early	ever	* really	* finally	along
later	o'clock	enough	together	against
mountain	piece	* numbers	few	* no one
side	* picture	* nothing	half	* everyone
ice	place	* thousands	* anyone	* everything
winter	* village	* difference	* anything	whose
buy	before	* I'd	* you'd	* what
wear	why	* I'll	* you'll	* what's
used	whether	* I'm	* you're	* let's
grown	* whenever	* I've	* you've	* themselves

LIST ③

Number of Words in the Word List: 220

LIST 3

mouse	* squirrel	creatures	fish	* chocolate
mice	goat	* butterfly	* rabbit	coffee
* puppy	* wolf	* dinosaur	* potato	flour
* puppies	* elephant	* monster	* potatoes	* apron
wash	* allow	swim	* arrived	threw
washing	* allowed	swimming	* offered	throw
washed	wished	rain	received	blew
dressed	* cannot	raining	grabbed	blow
* basket	lawn	shirt	* drawer	crash
* bowl	flowers	skirt	shelf	surprise
* board	patch	sheet	shelves	fright
brush	* vegetables	* curtain	stairs	* skeleton
fishing	believe	approach	lie	drag
float	* wondering	* recognised	lying	dragged
floated	* realised	remember	lay	* bury
drowned	* investigate	* remembered	laid	* buried
shock	* uncle	* February	* harbour	pony
* ambulance	* cousin	* months	beach	* ponies
* hospital	* grandfather	* holiday	* island	saddle
* oxygen	* neighbours	* Saturday	cave	stables
* climb	push	hopped	* whisper	* burst
tied	* pushed	hopping	* whispered	guard
falling	knocked	pretended	* whistle	* chase
slipped	smashed	hurt	screamed	* disappeared
pencil	* alphabet	* camera	* parliament	noise
* rubber	* calendar	* film	* palace	* policeman
* ruler	fractions	* submarine	* television	* uniform
* scissors	* graph	* magazine	* programme	* court
* dangerous	frightening	* favourite	* curious	lazy
* terrible	* poisonous	* orange	spare	dirty
massive	frightened	* purple	* quiet	* impossible
* enormous	scared	* visible	haunted	funny
* telephone	* visitor	* system	switch	flame
* message	* Germany	defence	* contact	volcano
rhyme	* London	* exhibition	* explosion	thunder
* tongue	* countries	* manager	bridge	* lightning
* motor	* excellent	* British	dining	* downstairs
racing	* wonderful	* Chinese	* hungry	* upstairs
tight	* fantastic	* Japanese	fried	* somewhere
* physical	* exciting	* Egyptian	* frozen	* everywhere
* bicycle	* hello	he'd	* aren't	* anyway
bike	* everybody	he'll	we'd	* somehow
race	* quietly	* he's	we'll	* anybody
track	* sixth	* they're	* we're	* somebody

ALPHABETICAL LIST ①

Number of Words in the Word List: 220

about	eyes	man	started
after	farm	married	stay
afternoon	father	me	story
all	fell	money	street
are	find	more	take
around	fire	morning	tea
ask	first	mother	teacher
asked	for	much	that
aunt	found	mum	that's
away	four	my	them
babies	from	name	then
baby	front	named	they
back	garden	new	things
bad	gave	next	think
bank	ghost	nice	this
be	giant	night	three
because	girl	no	time
bed	give	now	told
been	go	old	took
being	goes	once	tree
best	going	one	two
better	gold	or	upon
big	gone	other	very
black	good	our	walk
blue	had	out	walked
book	hair	over	walking
boy	hand	park	was
brother	happy	people	wasn't
bus	has	play	watch
but	have	played	watching
by	having	playing	water
call	he	please	way
called	help	put	we
came	her	queen	week
car	here	ready	well
castle	him	red	went
catch	himself	road	when
children	his	room	which
Christmas	home	round	while
come	house	said	white
coming	how	saw	who
could	just	say	will
couldn't	king	school	window
dad	lady	sea	with
dance	last	see	without
day	left	seen	woke
did	like	she	woman
didn't	little	shop	wood
dinner	live	sister	work
do	lived	sleep	would
dog	long	so	wouldn't
don't	look	some	year
door	looked	someone	yes
down	made	something	you
eat	make	start	your

109

© LDA ACE Spelling Activities

ALPHABETICAL LIST ❷

Number of Words in the Word List: 220

across	early	line	shoes
aeroplane	ears	listen	short
against	enough	listened	should
air	even	lonely	shouted
along	ever	love	side
already	every	machine	sitting
alright	everyone	many	slowly
also	everything	maybe	smaller
animals	family	mean	snake
answer	few	meant	spoke
answered	field	meat	station
any	finally	meet	straight
anyone	finish	minutes	strange
anything	finished	mountain	sugar
balloon	fly	mouth	sure
beautiful	followed	music	table
before	foot	near	tell
behind	football	nearby	themselves
bird	getting	nearly	these
blood	group	no-one	those
boat	grown	nose	thousands
body	guess	nothing	tired
break	half	notice	together
breakfast	happen	numbers	true
breaking	happened	o'clock	try
broken	head	onto	trying
brought	hear	owner	understand
build	heart	passed	used
built	high	past	usual
buy	higher	person	usually
careful	hold	pick	village
chair	hole	picked	voice
closed	hope	picture	waiting
clothes	hoped	piece	wear
colour	hoping	place	what
coloured	horse	plane	what's
corner	husband	point	wheel
course	I'd	present	whenever
covered	I'll	pretty	whether
cried	I'm	prince	whole
cry	I've	princess	whose
dark	ice	pull	why
dead	idea	pulled	wide
dear	imagine	quickly	wife
die	interesting	quite	winter
died	its	radio	word
difference	jumped	read	world
different	killed	reading	write
does	kitchen	real	writing
doesn't	language	really	written
done	later	seemed	you'd
dragon	leave	sentence	you'll
drop	let's	seven	you're
dropped	life	shape	you've
dry	light	ship	young

ALPHABETICAL LIST ③

Number of Words in the Word List: 220

allow	Egyptian	lie	screamed
allowed	elephant	lightning	sheet
alphabet	enormous	London	shelf
ambulance	everybody	lying	shelves
anybody	everywhere	magazine	shirt
anyway	excellent	manager	shock
approach	exciting	massive	sixth
apron	exhibition	message	skeleton
aren't	explosion	mice	skirt
arrived	falling	monster	slipped
basket	fantastic	months	smashed
beach	favourite	motor	somebody
believe	February	mouse	somehow
bicycle	film	neighbours	somewhere
bike	fish	noise	spare
blew	fishing	offered	squirrel
blow	flame	orange	stables
board	float	oxygen	stairs
bowl	floated	palace	submarine
bridge	flour	parliament	surprise
British	flowers	patch	swim
brush	fractions	pencil	swimming
buried	fried	physical	switch
burst	fright	poisonous	system
bury	frightened	policeman	telephone
butterfly	frightening	ponies	television
calendar	frozen	pony	terrible
camera	funny	potato	they're
cannot	Germany	potatoes	threw
cave	goat	pretended	throw
chase	grabbed	programme	thunder
Chinese	grandfather	puppies	tied
chocolate	graph	puppy	tight
climb	guard	purple	tongue
coffee	harbour	push	track
contact	haunted	pushed	uncle
countries	he'd	quiet	uniform
court	he'll	quietly	upstairs
cousin	he's	rabbit	vegetables
crash	hello	race	visible
creatures	holiday	racing	visitor
curious	hopped	rain	volcano
curtain	hopping	raining	wash
dangerous	hospital	realised	washed
defence	hungry	received	washing
dining	hurt	recognised	we'd
dinosaur	impossible	remember	we'll
dirty	investigate	remembered	we're
disappeared	island	rhyme	whisper
downstairs	Japanese	rubber	whispered
drag	knocked	ruler	whistle
dragged	laid	saddle	wished
drawer	lawn	Saturday	wolf
dressed	lay	scared	wonderful
drowned	lazy	scissors	wondering

ANSWER SHEETS

PRACTICE WITH LONG VOWEL SOUNDS

ANSWER SHEET PAGE **17**

(a) FOOD

1. toast 208	6. pastry 147	11. sweet 169	16. cream 155
2. ice-cream 183	7. savoury 149	12. rice 189	17. loaf 201
3. roll 206	8. muesli 217	13. oats 203	18. fruit 214
4. flavour 142	9. gravy 143	14. soup 221	19. plaice 147
5. cake 139	10. meat 164	15. cheese 155	20. tasty 151

(b) IN THE COUNTRY

1. lake 145	6. stream 169	11. pool 219	16. drainage 140
2. field 158	7. wheat 174	12. rye 189	17. haystack 144
3. acorn 137	8. oak 203	13. tree 172	18. leaves 163
4. root 220	9. toadstool 208	14. flies 181	19. spider 190
5. stone 207	10. bluebells 211	15. nightingale 187	20. snake 149

(c) SPORT

1. team 172	6. crew 212	11. race 148	16. skiing 169
2. skating............. 149	7. rowing 206	12. climbing 178	17. glider 182
3. height 182	8. diving 178	13. player 147	18. bowler 195
4. fielder 158	9. boot 211	14. try 192	19. goal 199
5. snooker 221	10. rival 189	15. losing 216	20. rules 220

(d) OCCUPATIONS

1. playwright 147	6. director 178	11. agent 137	16. poet................ 204
2. waiter 152	7. cleaner 155	12. labourer 145	17. dealer 156
3. salesman 149	8. librarian 185	13. student 221	18. jeweller 178
4. miner 186	9. grocer 199	14. newsagent 218	19. painter 147
5. preacher 166	10. fireman 181	15. pirate 188	20. leader............. 163

(e) TRAVEL

1. railway 148	6. road 206	11. pony 204	16. plane 147
2. scooter 221	7. bicycle 177	12. flight 181	17. cruise 212
3. breakdown 138	8. timetable 192	13. train 151	18. driver 178
4. motorist 202	9. wheels 174	14. pilot 188	19. vehicle 173
5. ocean 203	10. route 220	15. detour 156	20. scenery 169

PRACTICE WITH SHORT VOWEL SOUNDS

(a) WILDLIFE

1. butterfly 116	6. vixen 91	11. winkle 92	16. thrush 133
2. moth 105	7. cub 118	12. cockle 96	17. dove 120
3. squirrel 87	8. otter 106	13. mussel 126	18. swan 111
4. badger 5	9. jellyfish 42	14. lobster 104	19. kestrel 42
5. fox 100	10. crab 7	15. sparrow 25	20. slug 130

(b) HOSPITAL

1. ambulance 1	6. splint 87	11. health 40	16. drug 120
2. bandage 5	7. temperature . 52	12. lung 125	17. tablet 28
3. injury 72	8. blood 116	13. oxygen 106	18. pill 82
4. fracture 12	9. vaccine 29	14. scalpel 25	19. medication ... 44
5. limb 79	10. stethoscope .. 50	15. unconscious ... 134	20. stomach 130

(c) WINTER

1. frost 100	6. gloves 122	11. decorate 34	16. mistletoe 80
2. shiver 87	7. anorak 1	12. presents 46	17. berries 32
3. wintry 92	8. robin 110	13. tinsel 90	18. sledge 50
4. blizzard 57	9. Christmas 59	14. glisten 70	19. pantomime ... 22
5. slush 130	10. carolling 7	15. holly 102	20. January 18

(d) HOLIDAYS

1. sand 25	6. suntan 130	11. tent 52	16. visit 91
2. bucket 116	7. cottage 96	12. caravan 7	17. exhibition 36
3. paddle 22	8. fishing 68	13. disco 61	18. restaurant 48
4. swimming 87	9. camping 7	14. shopping 111	19. customs 118
5. deckchair 34	10. rucksack 129	15. trip 90	20. luggage 125

(e) GAMES AND PASTIMES

1. cricket 59	6. badminton 5	11. snap 25	16. rugby 129
2. chess 33	7. squash 111	12. dominoes 99	17. boxing 95
3. golf 101	8. netball 45	13. lotto 104	18. sledging 50
4. hockey 102	9. putting 128	14. skipping 87	19. stilts 87
5. tennis 52	10. jigsaws 77	15. football 121	20. juggling 124

PRACTICE WITH MIXED LONG AND SHORT

VOWEL SOUNDS (1)

(a) SCHOOL

1. cloakroom 196	6. lesson 43	11. lunch 125	16. copy 96
2. desk 34	7. bell 32	12. monitor 105	17. science 190
3. seat 169	8. break 138	13. prefect 166	18. mathematics 20
4. teacher 172	9. snack 25	14. jotter 103	19. games 143
5. subject 130	10. queue 219	15. notes 202	20. music 217

(b) DRINKS

1. coke 196	6. chocolate 96	11. shandy 25	16. brandy 5
2. lemonade 43	7. grapefruit 143	12. beer 154	17. alcoholic 1
3. milk 80	8. juice 216	13. cider 178	18. fizzy 68
4. coffee 96	9. wine 193	14. scotch 111	19. tonic 113
5. tea 172	10. punch 128	15. whisky 92	20. soda 207

(c) GUY FAWKES

1. evening 157	6. sticks 87	11. heat 160	16. banger 5
2. clothes 196	7. matches 20	12. bake 138	17. fuse 214
3. fire 181	8. light 185	13. sausages 111	18. taper 151
4. wood 136	9. flame 142	14. fireworks 181	19. glow 199
5. paper 147	10. crackle 7	15. colours 118	20. embers 36

(d) MOUNTAINS

1. peak 166	6. huge 215	11. precipice 46	16. crag 7
2. massive 20	7. summit 130	12. sheer 169	17. crevice 33
3. rugged 129	8. ridge 84	13. edge 36	18. trail 151
4. boulders 195	9. slope 207	14. torrent 113	19. scramble 25
5. pinnacle 82	10. avalanche 1	15. rocky 110	20. gully 122

(e) THE RAILWAY STATION

1. ticket 90	6. platform 22	11. diesel 156	16. sleeper 169
2. office 106	7. notice 202	12. carriage 7	17. signal 87
3. clock 96	8. timetable 192	13. train 151	18. buffers 116
4. case 139	9. kiosk 162	14. rails 148	19. bridge 57
5. trolley 113	10. engine 36	15. whistle 92	20. taxi 28

PRACTICE WITH MIXED LONG AND SHORT

VOWEL SOUNDS ❷

(a) FUN

1. smile 190	6. skipping 87	11. acting 1	16. chuckling 118
2. party 233	7. kissing 78	12. painting 147	17. giggling 70
3. happy 16	8. hugging 123	13. joke 201	18. merry 44
4. mirth 249	9. clown 277	14. tease 172	19. cartoon 227
5. joyful 272	10. tumbling 133	15. tickle 90	20. comic 96

(b) ON THE FARM

1. tractor 28	6. yard 235	11. corn 258	16. cattle 7
2. plough 282	7. orchard 264	12. barley 226	17. bullock 116
3. furrow 121	8. hedgerow 40	13. crop 96	18. sheep 169
4. fertiliser 246	9. harvest 230	14. dairy 237	19. goose 214
5. slurry 130	10. grain 143	15. herd 247	20. turkey 253

(c) WATER

1. waves 152	6. calm 227	11. whirlpool 255	16. trickle 90
2. splash 25	7. smooth 221	12. current 118	17. pour 265
3. spray 149	8. tranquil 28	13. squirt 252	18. still 87
4. choppy 96	9. river 84	14. jet 42	19. sparkling 234
5. rough 129	10. flow 198	15. fountain 279	20. pure 219

(d) FLOWERS

1. snowdrop 207	6. tulip 222	11. lily 79	16. foxglove 100
2. cowslip 277	7. marigold 20	12. lavender 19	17. thistle 90
3. hyacinth 182	8. pansy 22	13. heather 40	18. poppy 108
4. crocus 196	9. carnation 227	14. gorse 261	19. buttercup 116
5. daffodil 10	10. orchid 264	15. broom 211	20. daisy 140

(e) TREES

1. chestnut 33	6. birch 243	11. fir 246	16. oak 203
2. beech 154	7. ash 1	12. pine 188	17. olive 106
3. willow 92	8. palm 233	13. spruce 221	18. hazel 144
4. sycamore 87	9. holly 102	14. yew 224	19. mulberry 126
5. poplar 108	10. larch 231	15. bay 138	20. maple 146

SPELLINGS FOR SOUNDS

ANSWER SHEET

PAGE 21
1. axle
2. banned
3. camel
4. carrot
5. chapter
6. expand
7. fragile
8. franc
9. gamble
10. hammock
11. language
12. manner
13. married
14. panda
15. scratch

PAGE 23
1. again
2. bench
3. cellar
4. chemist
5. debt
6. exit
7. friend
8. guest
9. leisure
10. lesson
11. meadow
12. pedal
13. petrol
14. refuge
15. thread

PAGE 25
1. bridge
2. build
3. Christmas
4. crystal
5. filthy
6. hymn
7. kitchen
8. liquid
9. minute
10. pistol
11. ribbon
12. ring
13. symbols
14. villain
15. witch

PAGE 27
1. bomb
2. conquer
3. dolphin
4. glossy
5. knocked
6. knot
7. lobster
8. mosque
9. novel
10. olive
11. omelette
12. profit
13. quarry
14. squash
15. watt

PAGE 29
1. among
2. blush
3. budgie
4. currant
5. enough
6. gloves
7. grumpy
8. insult
9. plum
10. nun
11. rubbish
12. skull
13. some
14. troubles
15. upstairs

PAGE 31
1. ache
2. ancient
3. break
4. cradle
5. exhale
6. famous
7. gait
8. grate
9. hazy
10. jail
11. laid
12. mail
13. mistake
14. tray
15. weight

PAGE 33
1. appear
2. beetle
3. creak
4. deer
5. deceive
6. eager
7. equal
8. frequent
9. keyhole
10. leased
11. meter
12. needle
13. peace
14. queasy
15. sieze

PAGE 35
1. biceps
2. bridle
3. buyer
4. cyclist
5. dilute
6. dye
7. enquire
8. guidance
9. idol
10. lightning
11. might
12. pylon
13. tide
14. tire
15. vibrate

PAGE 37
1. bold
2. crowbar
3. dough
4. frozen
5. glow
6. grown-up
7. loan
8. moan
9. ocean
10. poach
11. rows
12. snowdrop
13. sole
14. throne
15. yolk

PAGE 39
1. amuse
2. beauty
3. bruise
4. choose
5. cruise
6. dew
7. Europe
8. gloomy
9. hooves
10. juice
11. new
12. nuisance
13. pollute
14. rhubarb
15. shoot

PAGE 41
1. arc
2. barley
3. carpet
4. carton
5. catarrh
6. farther
7. guitar
8. harpoon
9. harvest
10. heart
11. lager
12. parcel
13. scarf
14. sergeant
15. varnish

PAGE 43
1. aware
2. bare
3. barely
4. careless
5. daring
6. fare
7. farewell
8. hare
9. parent
10. prepare
11. repair
12. scary
13. stare
14. there
15. where

PAGE 45	PAGE 47	PAGE 49	PAGE 51
1. absurd	1. awful	1. avoid	1. allowed
2. alert	2. board	2. boiling	2. bough
3. birth	3. daughter	3. buoy	3. coward
4. burglar	4. force	4. choice	4. crowd
5. colonel	5. fortune	5. coin	5. drowsy
6. dirty	6. gorgeous	6. employ	6. flower
7. earn	7. haunt	7. foyer	7. foul
8. fur	8. hawk	8. hoist	8. hour
9. gurgle	9. mourning	9. joyful	9. mouth
10. journal	10. naughty	10. ointment	10. plough
11. murder	11. saucer	11. oyster	11. rounders
12. murmur	12. shore	12. poison	12. rowdy
13. perfume	13. stalk	13. rejoice	13. sprout
14. purchase	14. walk	14. soiled	14. thousand
15. world	15. war	15. toil	15. trowel

SPELLING FOR SOUND PUZZLES

ANSWER SHEET

PAGE 53

raisin
greyhound
daisy
potato
playmate
fragrant
complaint

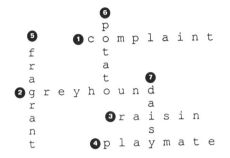

PAGE 54

skier
tweezers
machine
creeper
sphere
grieve
cedar

PAGE 55

strive
oblige
private
nylon
migrate
frightened
riot

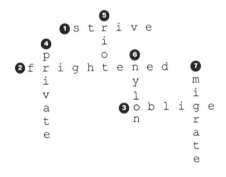

PAGE 56

doughnut
snowman
diploma
photograph
trophy
grocer
blowlamp

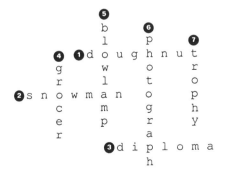

hoover
sewage
brute
rhubarb
futile
tomb
include

```
                        ⑥              ⑦
                        r              s
                     ①h o o v e r      w
                  ⑤              a      a
            ④     f              r      g
            i     u              b      e
            n   ②t o m b
            c     i
            l     l
          ③b r u t e
            u
            d
            e
```

departure
tarmac
sardine
sharpen
largest
charcoal
scarlet

```
            ⑤                    ⑦
     ①s a r d i n e   ⑥          t
            e         s          a
     ②s h a r p e n ③c h a r c o a l
            a         a          m
            r         r          a
            t         l          c
            u         e
          ④l a r g e s t
            e
```

scarce
staircase
warehouse
pharaoh
haircut
fairground
various

```
                        ⑥
                        s
                        t
                  ①v a r i o u s
                        r
                        c      ⑦
                ②p h a r a o h  f
                        s      i
            ③s c a r c e        r
                  ④h a i r c u t g
                        o        o
                  ⑤w a r e h o u s e
                        u
                        n
                        d
```

vermin
thirsty
world
learning
purple
suburban
nasturtium

```
            ⑤                        ⑦
            t                        l
            h            ⑥           e
      ①v e r m i n       n            a
            i            a            r
            s          ②s u b u r b a n
            t            t            i
            y            u            n
                  ③w o r l d          g
                         t
                         i
                   ④p u r p l e
                         m
```

122

wharf
wardrobe
forecast
cautious
strawberry
fourth
dormouse

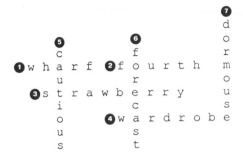

```
                                                    ❼
                                                    d
                      ❺                ❻            o
                      c                f            r
          ❶w h a r f  ❷f o u r t h     m
                      u                r            o
          ❸s t r a w b e r r y         u
                      i                c            s
                      o    ❹w a r d r o b e
                      u                a
                      s                s
                                       t
```

poison
moisture
buoyant
embroiderer
joinery
voyage
employment

```
                ❺
                m
          ❶j o i n e r y
                i        ❻
                s        m
                t   ❷b u o y a n t
                u        r
                r   ❸p o i s o n  ❼
                e        i        v
                         d        o
                    ❹e m p l o y m e n t
                         r        y
                                  a
                                  g
                                  e
```

powerful
howled
cowboy
loudest
voucher
trousers
showery

```
                              ❻        ❼
                              h        l
                   ❹          ❶c o w b o y
                   v          o        u
          ❷p o w e r f u l    w        d
                   u        ❺ l        e
                   c        t h        s
          ❸s h o w e r y    r o        t
                   e        o w
                   r        u l
                            s e
                            e d
                            r
                            s
```

123

CAR REGISTRATION GAME

ANSWER SHEET

PAGE 64

1. heavy
2. bacon
3. body
4. reward
5. woman
6. bracelet
7. ripen
8. secret

1

b	a	c	o	n	✸	✸	✸
w	o	m	a	n	✸	✸	✸
r	e	w	a	r	d	✸	✸
b	r	a	c	e	l	e	t
b	o	d	y	✸	✸	✸	✸
h	e	a	v	y	✸	✸	✸
s	e	c	r	e	t	✸	✸
r	i	p	e	n	✸	✸	✸

PAGE 65

1. ketchup
2. nightfall
3. ostrich
4. exhaust
5. fashion
6. whirlpool
7. reason
8. wicket

2

w	h	i	r	l	p	o	o	l
e	x	h	a	u	s	t	✸	✸
o	s	t	r	i	c	h	✸	✸
n	i	g	h	t	f	a	l	l
k	e	t	c	h	u	p	✸	✸
f	a	s	h	i	o	n	✸	✸
r	e	a	s	o	n	✸	✸	✸
w	i	c	k	e	t	✸	✸	✸

PAGE 66

1. leopard
2. dandruff
3. ocean
4. gorgeous
5. jiffy
6. ruby
7. reindeer
8. dungeon

3

r	e	i	n	d	e	e	r
r	u	b	y	✸	✸	✸	✸
d	u	n	g	e	o	n	✸
g	o	r	g	e	o	u	s
o	c	e	a	n	✸	✸	✸
j	i	f	f	y	✸	✸	✸
d	a	n	d	r	u	f	f
l	e	o	p	a	r	d	✸

TRICKY WORD ENDINGS

ANSWER SHEET

PAGE 67

1. jailer
2. motor
3. lever
4. liar
5. donor
6. pillar

1

```
p  e  f  l  a  r  i  q  s  o
d  t  e  f  a  r  m  e  r  t
l  g  p  i  r  s  o  n  a  e
e  d  o  u  v  o  t  e  r  n
s  p  o  d  o  n  o  r  a  j
l  c  i  n  u  r  o  z  a  i
e  a  t  l  b  k  l  e  o  l
v  s  u  n  l  c  a  i  r  e
e  c  k  f  y  a  i  l  a  r
r  l  m  o  w  e  r  s  t  r
```

PAGE 68

1. harden
2. toughen
3. cousin
4. bacon
5. blacken
6. talon

2

```
e  b  l  a  c  k  e  n  d  o
s  r  i  p  w  r  s  t  o  s
d  y  s  t  o  r  u  n  s  e
c  e  b  i  m  e  t  r  i  a
w  o  e  h  a  r  d  e  n  s
a  b  u  p  n  s  i  s  i  o
y  a  s  s  e  t  a  l  o  n
o  c  c  a  i  n  t  l  e  d
r  o  t  t  e  n  r  e  f  i
s  n  u  t  o  u  g  h  e  n
```

PAGE 69

1. nation
2. occupation
3. collision
4. session
5. motion
6. passion
7. magician
8. abbreviation
9. solution
10. optician

3

```
m  o  t  i  o  n  l  f  a  v  o  t
a  b  b  r  e  v  i  a  t  i  o  n
g  p  c  r  e  a  t  s  i  o  c  o
i  a  o  p  t  i  f  v  a  p  c  p
c  l  t  s  a  u  e  x  l  t  u  s
i  s  l  b  i  n  t  a  o  i  p  e
a  i  w  f  o  r  a  t  t  c  a  s
n  o  s  u  r  e  n  t  i  i  t  s
i  n  s  i  l  t  o  d  i  o  i  i
o  s  o  l  u  t  i  o  n  a  o  o
n  i  n  a  t  i  o  n  t  o  n  n
s  e  c  r  e  t  i  n  s  i  d  e
```

PAGE 70

1. discovery
2. nursery
3. satisfactory
4. extraordinary
5. recovery
6. complimentary
7. mastery
8. history
9. showery
10. victory

4

```
w  d  i  s  c  o  v  e  r  y  e  r  y
e  m  b  r  o  i  d  e  r  y  a  h  e
v  n  a  v  m  e  m  o  r  h  g  s  s
e  u  x  i  p  m  i  l  t  i  r  d  t
r  n  c  l  a  e  n  v  s  a  i  m
y  s  a  t  i  s  f  a  c  t  o  r  y
s  e  l  o  m  t  e  r  y  o  r  e  s
h  r  o  r  e  e  n  t  s  r  d  c  t
o  y  i  y  n  r  v  o  r  y  i  t  e
w  a  n  n  t  y  t  a  r  y  n  o  r
e  x  t  r  a  o  r  d  i  n  a  r  y
r  u  r  e  r  e  c  o  v  e  r  y  o
y  e  y  a  y  i  n  e  t  r  y  p  t
```

125

DOUBLES OR SINGLES

PAGE 71

1. manner
2. pepper
3. pilot
4. scooter
5. bullet
6. written
7. hammer
8. lapel
9. butter
10. totem

1

PAGE 72

1. lettuce
2. status
3. annoy
4. toilet
5. liner
6. drummer
7. super
8. lemon
9. illness
10. halo

2

FIND THE MIDDLE SYLLABLE

ANSWER SHEET

PAGE 73

1. parachute
2. entangled
3. bachelor
4. mascara
5. valiant
6. tapestry
7. javelin
8. battleship
9. subtraction
10. advertise
11. abandon
12. handkerchief
13. angrily
14. animals
15. familiar

PAGE 74

1. inspector
2. complexion
3. skeleton
4. wellington
5. terrify
6. delicate
7. merriment
8. recipe
9. penalty
10. venison
11. restaurant
12. flexible
13. offensive
14. pessimist
15. Celsius

PAGE 75

1. brigadier
2. flamingo
3. exquisite
4. neglectful
5. sinister
6. rickety
7. tributary
8. vanilla
9. intention
10. revolver
11. continue
12. decision
13. division
14. discussion
15. difficult

PAGE 76

1. bronchitis
2. corridor
3. solitude
4. volunteer
5. tomahawk
6. hospital
7. gossiping
8. mosquito
9. astonished
10. contradict
11. monument
12. probably
13. properly
14. doggedly
15. colossal

PAGE 77

1. buffalo
2. muscular
3. repulsive
4. wonderful
5. bumble bee
6. customer
7. abundance
8. multiply
9. unconscious
10. wondering
11. bungalow
12. another
13. discourage
14. sultana
15. suddenly

PAGE 78

1. patiently
2. masonry
3. stationery
4. amazement
5. narrator
6. labelling
7. mistaken
8. neighbourhood
9. dangerous
10. tablespoon
11. shakily
12. impatient
13. vacation
14. frustration
15. stadium

PAGE 79

1. preceded
2. achievement
3. vehement
4. weariness
5. vehicle
6. tedious
7. previous
8. cereal
9. reassure
10. equally
11. conceited
12. scenery
13. lenient
14. sincerely
15. media

PAGE 80

1. exciting
2. migrating
3. triangle
4. xylophone
5. library
6. assignment
7. gigantic
8. horizon
9. livelihood
10. triumphant
11. ivory
12. bribery
13. financial
14. designer
15. survivor

PAGE 81

1. aroma
2. immobile
3. ownership
4. devotion
5. groceries
6. foliage
7. atrocious
8. sociable
9. loneliness
10. emotion
11. odious
12. coconut
13. ferocious
14. jovial
15. viola

PAGE 82

1. museum
2. endurance
3. duplicate
4. tubular
5. amusement
6. jubilee
7. commuter
8. lubricate
9. ruinous
10. pneumatic
11. beautiful
12. intruder
13. secluded
14. fugitive
15. luminous

PAGE 83

1. spectacles
2. exhausted
3. vigorous
4. architect
5. lemonade
6. bicycle
7. marvellous
8. gorilla
9. burglary
10. foreigner
11. orchestra
12. mosaic
13. certainly
14. mountainous
15. appointment

FIND THE TWO MIDDLE SYLLABLES

PAGE 84

1. victorious
2. impossible
3. population
4. environment
5. development
6. superstition
7. photography
8. identical
9. ridiculous
10. favourable
11. kilometre
12. minority
13. embarrassing
14. memorial
15. spontaneous

1

PAGE 85

1. notorious
2. coronation
3. accumulate
4. temporary
5. proprietor
6. economies
7. communicate
8. vegetation
9. hilarious
10. astronomy
11. supermarket
12. carnivorous
13. tonsilitis
14. peculiar
15. horizontal

2

WORDS WITHIN WORDS

ANSWER SHEET

The following answers are those which can be found in the ACE Spelling Dictionary. Other correct answers (**e.g.** thundercloud) are, of course, acceptable.

1.	safe	safeguard
2.	care	careful, carefully, carelessly
3.	fit	fitted, fitting, fitness
4.	fun	funfair, funnier
5.	rock	rockery, rockier, rockiest
6.	thunder	thunderous, thunderstorm
7.	net	netball, netted, network
8.	rain	rainbow, raincoat, rainfall, rainier, raining
9.	down	downfall, downhill, downright, downstream, downward
10.	earth	earthenware, earthquake, earthworm
11.	shop	shopkeeper, shopping
12.	slip	slipper, slippered, slippery, slipstone
13.	foot	football, foothill, foothold, footpath
14.	bright	brightened, brightest
15.	some	somebody, somehow, someone, something, sometime, sometimes, somewhat, somewhere

The following answers are those which can be found in the ACE Spelling Dictionary. Other correct answers (**e.g.** downcast) are, of course, acceptable.

1.	circle	circulate, circulation, circulatory, circumference, circumscribe, circumstances
2.	dirt	dirtied, dirtier, dirties, dirtiest
3.	cheer	cheerful, cheering
4.	image	imaginary, imaginative, imagines
5.	whole	wholemeal, wholesale, wholesome
6.	dread	dreadful, dreadfully
7.	infect	infection
8.	memory	memorable, memorandum, memorised
9.	chaos	chaotically
10.	govern	government
11.	mercy	merciful, mercifully, merciless
12.	greed	greedier, greediest, greedily
13.	science	scientific, scientifically
14.	mount	mountain, mountaineering, mountainous, mountainside, mountaintop
15.	agree	agreement

FIND THE BASEWORD OR THE ROOT

PAGE 88

1. a   polite
2. b   explode
3. b   mine
4. a   plant
5. b   series
6. b   scorn
7. b   globe
8. b   rely
9. a   simple
10. b   fiction

1

PAGE 89

1. b   mortal
2. a   liberate
3. a   joy
4. b   optic
5. b   navigate
6. a   view
7. b   stream
8. b   employ
9. a   less
10. b   accept

2

INTRODUCING THE PARTS OF SPEECH

PAGE 90

1. brigade
2. blaze
3. bale
4. bracelet

1. hostess
2. hotel
3. home
4. hosepipe

1. drum
2. dummy
3. dungarees
4. dove

1. furniture
2. fern
3. furnace
4. fertiliser

PAGE 91

1. meat
2. machine
3. measles
4. meal

1. square
2. scarecrow
3. share
4. staircase

1. crucifix
2. computer
3. cucumber
4. clue

1. cloud
2. councillor
3. crown
4. couch

PAGE 92

1. flavoured
2. framed
3. faded
4. forgave

1. peck
2. patted
3. pedalling
4. pressed

1. counting
2. cowered
3. crown
4. crowded

1. trudging
2. thumped
3. tunnelling
4. touch

PAGE 93

1. searching
2. stirred
3. surging
4. shirk

1. tie
2. timetabled
3. tried
4. time

1. besieged
2. breed
3. breathe
4. beat

1. chopping
2. cross
3. concentrate
4. complicate

PAGE 94

1. polite
2. private
3. psychic
4. primary

1. ravenous
2. ramshackle
3. ragged
4. Random

1. toxic
2. tropical
3. toffee
4. throbbing

1. naughty
2. normal
3. nautical
4. northern

PAGE 95

1. Unfortunately
2. unconventionally
3. undoubtedly
4. underfoot

1. shyly
2. scientifically
3. silently
4. slightly

1. temporarily
2. technically
3. torrentially
4. terribly

1. tactfully
2. tragically
3. tyrannically
4. Thankfully